Headless
and Other Stories

Edited by Barbara Bleiman and Sabrina Broadbent

Edited by Barbara Bleiman and Sabrina Broadbent

Activities by Barbara Bleiman and Sabrina Broadbent
Additional material by Jenny Grahame and Michael Simons

Designed and typeset by Liz Elwin
Cover by Dave Bradshaw, Push Design
Printed by Redwood Books, Trowbridge Wiltshire

© The English and Media Centre 1996
136 Chalton Street, London NW1 1RX
ISBN 0 907016 52 9

Acknowledgements

We wish to thank the following who have kindly given permission for the use of copyright material:

'Kreativ Riting', from *In a Dark Room with a Stranger* (Hamish Hamilton 1993), © Brian McCabe 1993. Reproduced by permission of Penguin Books Ltd.; 'My Son the Fanatic', first published in *The New Yorker,* March 1994. © Hanif Kureishi 1994. Reproduced by permission of the author c/o Rogers, Coleridge & White Ltd.; 'American Dreams', from *The Fat Man in History* (September 1996), © Peter Carey. Reproduced by permission of Faber and Faber Ltd.; 'The Potato Gatherers', from *Selected Stories* (1979), © Brian Friel. Reproduced by permission of The Gallery Press, Loughcrew, Oldcastle, County Meath, Ireland; 'A Basket Full of Wallpaper', from *Fishing the Sloe-Black River* (Phoenix House 1994), © Colum McCann. Reproduced by permission of Curtis Brown Ltd., London; 'Joebell and America', from *A Brief Conversion and other stories* (Heinemann Caribbean Writers Series 1988), © Earl Lovelace. Reproduced by permission of Simpson Fox Associates, London; 'White Places', from *Bad Girls,* © Mary Flanagan. Reproduced by permission of Jonathan Cape Ltd, Random House; 'Dear George', from *Heavy Weather* (Heinemann), © Helen Simpson. Reproduced by permission of Reed Consumer Books Ltd., London; 'Mrs Turner Cutting the Grass', by Carol Shields, reproduced from *Various Miracles* published by Fourth Estate Ltd © 1995; 'Headless', © Brian Aldiss 1995. Reproduced by permission of Curtis Brown, London; 'A Small Good Thing' by Raymond Carver, from *Shortcuts*, first published as a paperback original in Great Britain 1993 by Harvill. © Tess Gallagher 1993. Reproduced by permission of The Harvill Press, London; 'Spirit' reproduced with permission of Curtis Brown Ltd, London on behalf of Janet Frame. Copyright © 1951 Janet Frame; 'The Two Grandmothers', by Olive Senior, from *Arrival of the Snake Woman and other stories* (Longman). Reproduced by permission of Addison, Wesley, Longman. 'Along the River', first published in *Omni Best Science Fiction Three:* © Ursula Le Guin, 1993, reprinted by permission of the author and the author's agent, Virginia Kidd.

We have made every effort to obtain copyright permission. We would be grateful to hear from anyone we have been unable to contact.

Contents

Introduction

The short story at KS4

Good short stories have always been part of the staple diet of English classrooms. Set text lists for Literature and required reading for English have become increasingly prescriptive and focused on the past. It is important for English teachers therefore, to continue to offer recent, inspiring and entertaining fiction that will provoke lively, engaged responses from 14–16 year olds, and help them to develop in English as well as Literature. The arguments for teaching short stories are numerous:

- Given the constraints of time, short stories provide a manageable way of giving students a complete experience of a text in one sitting.
- Their brevity means that a collection of stories can introduce students to the *range* of literary forms, writing from different cultures and perspectives that are required within the National Curriculum and GCSE specifications.
- Short stories can be the spark for successful group work, oral work and a range of different kinds of writing that can contribute to pupils' development in English as well as Literature.
- It can be more manageable to explore questions of language, authorial intention, structure and other aspects of a writer's craft through a short story than through longer texts.
- Short stories can offer starting points for wider reading and scope for manageable comparative work, which has become a key element in Literature syllabuses.
- They can provide ways into set texts. A good contemporary story can be a useful springboard for studying a pre-twentieth century text.
- Preparation for work on unseen texts in exams can also be achieved through work on a range of short texts, including the short story.

Writing that signals the times

Most of the stories in this collection are by living writers; most have been written within the past five years. The writers are among the most celebrated voices of the late twentieth century, yet many have not been widely anthologised for schools. The stories themselves were chosen because we felt they would intrigue, challenge and entertain young readers. The subject matter is varied, but several stories offer different perspectives on a similar issue and could be paired for comparative work. The stories are arranged alphabetically by writer.

Working on the stories

Each story is followed by a few pages of classroom activities. Whilst the text identifies whether activities should be undertaken before, during or after reading, not every story has activities for each of these stages. This reflects the fact that different stories require different treatment, and a rigid adherence to a pattern can become unnecessarily laborious. Many of the activities are designed to facilitate discussion in small groups. There is an emphasis on close reading and exploration of what it is that a writer is doing with character, with narrative and with language. Pupils are encouraged to think about the voice of the writer and compare it with other voices in other stories.

Comparative work

Towards the end of each activity there are suggestions for comparative work. To avoid repetition the activities sometimes refer pupils to a different story for a detailed description of the possibilities for comparison. As a simple guide to working across the anthology, this chart shows some of the more obvious connections between stories:

Childhood/growing up
The Potato Gatherers
White Places
A Basket Full of Wallpaper
The Two Grandmothers

Teenagers
American Dreams
Dear George
The Two Grandmothers
My Son the Fanatic
Kreativ Riting

Cultural identity
The Two Grandmothers
Joebell and America
My Son the Fanatic

Other worlds
Headless
Spirit
Along the River

The death of a child
The Schoolteacher's Guest
A Small Good Thing

Individuals and communities
The Schoolteacher's Guest
American Dreams
Joebell and America
A Basket Full of Wallpaper
Mrs. Turner Cutting the Grass

Unusual forms of narration
Spirit
The Two Grandmothers

Dreams of escape
American Dreams
Joebell and America

Boys and men
The Potato Gatherers
Joebell and America
Kreativ Riting
My Son the Fanatic
A Basket Full of Wallpaper

Girls
White Places
Dear George
The Two Grandmothers

American short stories
A Small Good Thing
White Places
Mrs. Turner Cutting the Grass

Caribbean short stories
Joebell and America
The Two Grandmothers

Irish short stories
The Potato Gatherers
A Basket Full of Wallpaper

Black and Asian writing
My Son the Fanatic
Joebell and America
The Two Grandmothers

Wider reading and GCSE set texts

Wider reading has been threatened by the constraints and requirements of the KS4 criteria. Despite this, it remains a significant way of pupils developing confidence and competence as readers and writers and should continue to be promoted for this reason.

The wider reading suggestions at the end of the activities on each story could be used in two ways. Firstly, they could be the basis for wider reading for coursework. Starting with a common text like a short story can be a good way of supporting independent reading and writing about texts. Pupils can draw on whole-class discussion and thinking, and extend this to other texts. Secondly, the short stories can be used as starting points and additional material to support the reading of set texts. For instance, if a class is about to study *Silas Marner* as a set text, 'A Basket Full of Wallpaper' might be a good starting point. Likewise, 'White Places' would be an interesting text to read alongside Susan Hill's *I'm the King of the Castle*, or the rather macabre, strange story 'The Schoolteacher's Guest' might make a useful companion to Hardy's *Wessex Tales*.

The suggestions for wider reading have been written in the light of the most recent GCSE syllabuses and contain a number of references to set texts that appear in those syllabuses. Wherever such texts are mentioned, they are identified with the symbol of a book [GCSE].

The writers and their stories

At the end of the book is a section giving information about each of the writers. Several have written accounts of what sparked off the story. They have been placed at the end of the book, so as not to pre-empt prediction work and pupils' own readings. However they would make an interesting focus after initial work on the text.

Note In American stories, American spellings have been kept, as in the original texts.

Headless

A vast crowd was gathering to see Flammerion behead himself. The TV people and Flammerion had rehearsed almost everything so that the event would go without a hitch. It was estimated that some 1.8 billion people would be watching: the largest TV audience since the nuking of North Korea.

Some people preferred to watch the event live. Seats in the stadium, highly priced, were booked months in advance.

Among the privileged were Alan Ibrox Kumar and his wife, Dorothea Kumar, the Yakaphrenia Lady. They discussed it as they flew in to Düsseldorf.

'Why is he giving all the proceeds to Children of Turkmenistan, for heaven's sake?' Alan demanded.

'The terrible earthquake... Surely you remember?'

'I remember, yes, yes. But Flammerion's European, isn't he?'

For answer, she said: 'Get me another gin, will you?' She had yet to reveal to him she was divorcing him directly after the beheading.

The Swedish Royal family had reserved two seats in a back row. They felt that Sweden should be represented at what was increasingly regarded – by the media at any rate – as an important event. The Swedish Government remained furious that their offer of a prominent site in Stockholm had been turned down by Flammerion's agent.

Fortunately, six Swedes, two of them women, had since volunteered to behead themselves, either in Stockholm or preferably Uppsala. They had named the charities they preferred.

Dr Eva Berger had booked a seat in the stadium on the day the box office opened. She had counselled Flammerion, advising against his drastic action on health grounds. When she realized she was unable to deflect him from his purpose, she begged him that at least a percentage of the proceeds go towards the Institute of Psychoanalysts. Flammerion had replied: 'I am offering you my psychiatric example. What else do you want? Don't be greedy.'

Later, Dr Berger had sold her seat for nineteen times the amount she had paid for it. She felt her integrity had paid off.

Dr Berger's feckless nephew, Leigh, happened to be a cleaner in the Dusseldorf stadium. 'Thank God I'm not on duty tonight,' he said. 'There'll be one hell of a mess. Blood everywhere.'

'That's what the public pay for,' said his boss. 'Blood has a whole vast symbolism behind it. It's not just a red liquid, son. You've heard of bad blood, and princes of the blood, and blood boiling, or things done in cold blood, haven't you? We've got a whole mythology on our hands, no less, tonight. And I need you to do an extra shift.'

Leigh looked hangdog and asked what they would do with the head when Flammerion had finished with it.

His boss told him it would be auctioned at Sotheby's in London.

Among those who were making money from the event was Cynthia Saladin. She had sold her story to the media worldwide. Most people on the globe were conversant with what Cynthia and Flammerion had done in bed. Cynthia had tried her best to entertain, and was now married to a Japanese businessman. Her book, *Did Circumcision Start Flammy Going Funny?*, had been rushed into print, and was available everywhere.

Flammerion was passably good-looking. Commentators remarked on the numbers of ugly men who had bought seats in the stadium. Among their numbers were Monty Wilding, the British film director whose face had been likened to a wrinkled plastic bag. Monty was boasting that his exploitation-flick, *Trouble Ahead*, was already at the editing stage.

The Green Party protested against the movie, and about the self-execution, claiming that it was worse than a blood-sport and would undoubtedly start a trend. British sportsmen, too, were up in arms. The beheading clashed with the evening of the Cup Final replay. F.A. IN HEAD-OFF COLLISION ran the headline in the *Sun*:

There were others in Britain equally incensed by what was taking place on the Continent. Among them were those who remained totally ignorant of the whereabouts of Turkmenistan.

As so often in times of trouble, people turned towards their solicitors, the Archbishop of Canterbury and Nick Ross for consolation – not necessarily in that order.

The Archbishop delivered a fine sermon on the subject, reminding the congregation that Jesus had given His life that we might live, and that that 'we' included the common people of England as well as the Tory party. Now here was another young man, Borgo Flammerion, prepared to give up his life for the suffering children of Central Asia – if that indeed was where Turkmenistan was situated.

It was true, the Archbishop continued, that Christ had not permitted Himself to be crucified before the television cameras, but that was merely an unfortunate accident of timing. The few witnesses of the Crucifixion whose words had come down to us were notoriously unreliable. Indeed, it was possible (as much must be readily admitted) that the whole thing was a cock-and-bull story. Had Christ postponed the event by a millennium or two, photography would have provided a reliable testament to His self-sacrifice, and then perhaps everyone in Britain would believe in Him, instead of just a lousy nine per cent.

Meanwhile, the Archbishop concluded, we should all pray for Flammerion, that the deed he contemplated be achieved without pain.

Visibly put out by this address, the British Prime Minister made an acid retort in the House of Commons on the following day. She said, amid general laughter, that at least *she* was not losing her head. She added that the Archbishop of Canterbury should ignore what went on in Europe and look to her own parish. Why, a murder had taken place in Canterbury just the previous month. Whatever might or might not be happening in Dusseldorf, one thing was certain: Great Britain was pulling out of recession.

This much-applauded speech was delivered only hours before Flammerion performed in public.

As the stadium began to fill, bands played solemn music and old Beatles hits. Coachloads of French people of all sexes arrived. The French took particular interest in 'L'Evenement Flammerion', claiming the performer to be of French descent, although born in St Petersburg of a Russian mother. This statement had irritated elements of the American press, who pointed out that there was a St Petersburg in Florida, too.

A belated move was afoot to have Flammerion extradited to Florida to be legally executed for Intended Suicide, now a capital offence.

The French, undeterred, filled the press with long articles of analysis, under such headings as FLAMMY: EST-IL PEDALE? T-shirts, depicting the hero with head and penis missing, were selling well.

The country which gained most from the event was Germany. Already a soap was running on TV called *Kopf Kaputt,* about an amusing Bavarian family, all of whom were busy buying chain-saws with which to behead each other. Some viewers read a political message into *Kopf Kaputt.*

Both the Red Cross and the Green Crescent paraded round the stadium. They had already benefited enormously from the publicity. The Green Crescent ambulances were followed by lorries on which lay young Turkmen victims of the earthquake in bloodstained bandages. They were cheered to the echo. All told, a festival air prevailed.

Behind the scenes, matters were almost as noisy. Gangs of well-wishers and autograph hunters queued for a sight of their hero. In another bunch stood professional men and women who hoped, even at this late hour, to dissuade Flammerion from his fatal act. Any number of objections to the act were raised. Among these objections were the moral repulsiveness of the act itself, its effect on children, the fact that Cynthia still loved her man, the fear of a riot should Flammerion's blade miss its mark, and the question whether the act was possible as Flammerion proposed it. Among the agitated objectors were cutlers, eager to offer a sharper blade.

None of these people, no priest, no sensation-seeker, no surgeon offering to replace the head immediately it was severed, was allowed into Flammerion's guarded quarters.

Borgo Flammerion sat in an office chair, reading a copy of the *Russian Poultry Dealer's Monthly*. As a teenager, he had lived on a poultry farm. Earning promotion, he had worked for a while in the slaughterhouse before emigrating to Holland, where he had robbed a patisserie.

He was dressed in a gold lamé blouson jacket, sable tights, and lace-up boots. His head was shaven: he had taken advice on this.

On the table before him lay a brand new cleaver, especially sharpened by a man from Geneva, a representative of the Swiss company which had manufactured the instrument. Flammerion glanced at this cleaver every so often, as he read about a startling new method of egg-retrieval. Figures on his digital watch writhed towards the hour of eight.

Behind him stood a nun, Sister Madonna, his sole companion in these last days. She was chosen because she had once made a mistaken pilgrimage to Ashkhabad, capital of Turkmenistan, believing she was travelling to Allahabad in India.

At a signal from the Sister, Flammerion closed his periodical. Rising, he took up the cleaver. He walked up the stairs with firm tread, to emerge into the dazzle of floodlights.

An American TV announcer dressed in a blood-red gown said sweetly: 'If your immediate viewing plans do not include decapitation this evening, may we advise you to look away for a few minutes.'

When the applause died, Flammerion took up a position between the chalk marks.

He bowed without smiling. When he whirled the cleaver to his right side, the blade glittered in the lights. The crowd fell silent as death.

Flammerion brought the blade up sharply, so that it sliced from throat to nape-of-neck. His head fell cleanly away from his body.

He remained standing for a moment, letting the cleaver drop from his grasp.

The stadium audience was slow to applaud. But all had gone exceptionally well, considering that Flammerion had had no proper rehearsal.

Brian Aldiss

Working on Headless

1. Predictions
● Make some predictions about what the story might be like from its title.
● Look at this list of people in the story. What do they suggest about the kind of world this might be?

Borgo Flammerion
Alan Ibrox Kumar
the Yakaphrenia Lady
Cynthia Saladin

2. A sci-fi world?
● How far into the future do you imagine it to be:

– 5 years?
– 10 years?
– 50 years?
– 100 years?

● Find three pieces of evidence in the story to back up your opinion.

3. A satire
● What do you think the story is satirising about today's society? You could think about the following headings and list ideas under each one:

– the media
– government
– social attitudes
– fame and stardom
– relations between the countries of the world

● Talk about whether you believe that our society could end up like the one Aldiss portrays in 'Headless'. Use each of the headings to structure your discussion.

● Satire is usually a humorous way of criticising something about the writer's society. These are some of the techniques that writers use in satire:

– exaggeration
– understatement
– shock tactics
– surprising the reader

Look through the story to see if you can find any examples of each of these techniques in the story.

4. Funny or serious?

● Divide up into groups, with half the groups looking for evidence that the story is funny and the other half looking for evidence that it is serious. When you are ready, re-organise yourselves into new groups containing even numbers of people on both sides of the argument. Present your evidence to each other and see if you can come to an agreement about your view of the story.

5. How the story is written

● Look closely at the opening and ending of the story, which are printed for you below.
Talk about what is interesting or unusual about the voice of the writer:

– how aware are you of his voice?
– what kind of information does he give the reader?
– what does he leave out?
– how does this compare with your expectations of beginnings and endings of narratives?

Opening

A vast crowd was gathering to see Flammerion behead himself. The TV people and Flammerion had rehearsed almost everything so that the event would go without a hitch. It was estimated that some 1.8 billion people would be watching: the largest TV audience since the nuking of North Korea.

Some people preferred to watch the event live. Seats in the stadium, highly priced, were booked months in advance.

Among the privileged were Alan Ibrox Kumar and his wife, Dorothea Kumar, the Yakaphrenia Lady. They discussed it as they flew in to Düsseldorf.

Ending

Flammerion brought the blade up sharply, so that it sliced from throat to nape-of-neck. His head fell cleanly away from his body.

He remained standing for a moment, letting the cleaver drop from his grasp.

The stadium audience was slow to applaud. But all had gone exceptionally well, considering that Flammerion had had no proper rehearsal.

- Skim through the rest of the story to look at how the writer develops the narrative. Find something to say about each of these headings:

– dialogue
– description
– how events are recounted
– whose voices we hear and how we hear them
– whether and how the writer's viewpoint is revealed to the reader

6. After the millennium

- Make a list of things about modern life and trends in Britain that worry you, annoy you or amuse you, e.g. homelessness, pollution, boy bands, Aids, killer bugs, ecstasy, home computers etc.
- Imagine scenes 20 years on and think about what might have happened in terms of each of these trends. Make up a story that makes the reader think about where society is going. You might put yourself into the story, imagining yourself and your life in twenty years' time:

– will you be single/married?
– will you have children?
– what sort of home/means of transport/job/leisure pursuits will you have?
– what kinds of attitudes/feelings will you have about the world around you?

7. Comparative work – other worlds

'Spirit' and 'American Dreams' are two other stories which mix fantasy and reality.
- Read the stories, then compare them in the ways suggested below.
- Talk about how you could complete this sentence for each story:

– In 'Headless', Brian Aldiss asks the question, 'What if............'
– In 'Spirit', Janet Frame asks the question, 'What if............'
– In 'American Dreams', Peter Carey asks the question, 'What if............'

Compare your sentences with those of other groups in the class.
- Look at the openings of each of the three stories. Compare them, using the list of ideas below to help you:

– whose voice is speaking and what kind of voice is it?
– what use is made of description and dialogue?
– what does the writer chose to focus on: characters, the situation, the events or anything else?
– is the tone of the writing humorous or serious, chatty or formal?

8. Comparative work – sci-fi

Brian Aldiss is well known as a science fiction writer. 'Along the River' by Ursula Le Guin was originally anthologised in a collection of sci-fi stories.
- What elements do these two stories share which suggest that they belong to the sci-fi genre?

9. Comparative work – meeting in the afterlife

● Imagine that Borgo Flammerion, (from 'Headless'), meets Spirit 350 (from 'Spirit') and a cook or a firelighter, (from 'Along the River'). They are all in the afterlife, where they have eternity stretching ahead to think back on the worlds they came from. They talk to each other about their lives and worlds.

● Write a playscript of their conversation for performance to the rest of the class.

10. Wider reading

● Brian Aldiss has written many other sci-fi stories. Other sci-fi short story writers you might try are Arthur C. Clarke, Ray Bradbury and Ursula Le Guin.

● *Daz 4 Zoe* by Robert Swindells is a novel set in a not-so-distant future world, telling the story of two teenagers living in a divided and threatening society and trying to escape from the ties of their own rigidly separated communities.

● *Not, Not, Not, Not, Not Enough Oxygen* by Caryl Churchill is a short play, originally written for radio, that is set in 2010 in 'the Londons', a bleak vision of a future world. It has some interesting similarities with 'Headless' and would make a good text to compare with it.

● H.G. Wells' short story, 'The Time Machine', is a famous nineteenth century sci-fi story that is still surprisingly relevant. He has also written 'The Stolen Bacillus' which appears in *The New Windmill Book of Nineteenth Century Short Stories*.

● Mary Shelley's novel *Frankenstein*, written in the early nineteenth century, creates a fantasy of scientific experimentation to create new life.

● George Orwell's *Nineteen Eighty-Four* and Aldous Huxley's *Brave New World* are both novels which use a future world to comment on the writer's own society.

● *Riddley Walker* by Russell Hoban is a demanding novel about the world after a nuclear holocaust, written in a strange post-holocaust language.

The Schoolteacher's Guest

The Schoolteacher Ines entered The Pearl of the Orient, deserted at this hour, walked to the counter where Riad Halabi was rolling up a bolt of bright-flowered cloth, and announced to him that she had just cut off the head of a guest in her boarding house. The merchant took out his white handkerchief and clapped it to his mouth.

'What did you say, Ines?'

'Exactly what you heard, Turk.'

'Is he dead?'

'Of course.'

'And now what are you going to do?'

'That's what I came to ask you,' she replied, tucking back a stray lock of hair.

'I think I'd better close the store,' sighed Riad Halabi.

The two had known each other so long that neither could remember the exact number of years, although both recalled every detail of the day their friendship had begun. At the time, Halabi had been one of those salesmen who wander the byways offering their wares, a commercial pilgrim without compass or fixed course, an Arab immigrant with a false Turkish passport, lonely, weary, with a palate split like a rabbit's and a subsequent longing to sit in the shadows. She had been a still-young woman with firm hips and proud shoulders, the town's only schoolteacher, and the mother of a twelve-year-old son born of a fleeting love affair. The boy was the centre of the schoolteacher's life; she cared for him with unwavering devotion but, barely masking her inclination to indulge him, applied to him the same norms of discipline she demanded of the other schoolchildren. She did not want anyone to be able to say she had brought him up badly; at the same time, she hoped to negate the father's legacy of waywardness and instead form her son to be of clear mind and generous

9

heart. The very evening on which Riad Halabi had driven into Agua Santa from one side of town, from the other a group of boys had carried in the body of schoolteacher Ines's son on an improvised stretcher. He had walked on to someone's property to pick up a fallen mango, and the owner, an outsider whom no one really knew, had fired a blast from his rifle meaning to scare the boy away but drilling a black hole in the middle of his forehead through which his life rapidly escaped. At that moment, the salesman had discovered his vocation for leadership and, without knowing how, had found himself at the centre of things, consoling the mother, organizing the funeral as if he were a member of the family, and calming the people to prevent them from tearing the perpetrator limb from limb. Meanwhile, the murderer, realizing that his life would be worth very little if he remained here, had fled, never meaning to return.

It was Riad Halabi who, the following morning, was at the head of the crowd that marched from the cemetery to the place where the boy had fallen. All the inhabitants of Agua Santa had spent that day hauling mangoes, which they threw through the windows until the house was filled from floor to ceiling. After a few weeks, the sun had fermented the fruit, which burst open spilling a viscous juice and impregnating the walls with a golden blood, a sweetish pus, that transformed the dwelling into a fossil of prehistoric dimensions, an enormous beast in process of putrefaction, tormented by the infinite diligence of the larvae and mosquitoes of decomposition.

The death of the boy, the role he had played during those days, and the welcome he had received in Agua Santa, had determined the course of Riad Halabi's life. He forgot his nomadic ancestry and remained in the village. There he opened a business, The Pearl of the Orient. He married, was widowed, married a second time, and continued his trade, while his reputation for being a just man steadily increased. Ines, in turn, educated several generations of children with the tenacious affection she would have bestowed upon her son, until her energies were spent; then she had stepped aside for teachers who arrived from the city with new primers, and retired. After leaving the schoolroom, she felt as if she had aged suddenly, as if time were accelerating; the days passed so quickly that she could not remember where the hours had gone.

'I go around in a daze, Turk. I'm dying and don't even know it,' she commented.

'You're as healthy as you ever were, Ines,' replied Riad Halabi. 'The problem is that you're bored. You should not be idle.' And he suggested she add a few rooms to her house and take in guests: 'We don't have a hotel in this town.'

'We don't have tourists, either,' she added.

'A clean bed and warm breakfast are a blessing for travellers.'

And so they had been, primarily for the truckdrivers for National Petroleum, who stayed the night in her boarding house when the fatigue and tedium of the road had filled their heads with hallucinations.

The schoolteacher Ines was the most respected matron in all Agua Santa. She had taught the town's children for several decades, which granted her the authority to intervene in all their lives and take them by the ear when she felt it necessary. Girls brought their boyfriends for her approval, husbands and wives came to her with their marital disagreements; she was counsellor, arbiter, and judge in all the town's problems. Her authority, in fact, was mightier than that of the priest, the doctor, or the police. No one stopped her from the exercise of that power. On one occasion she had stalked into the jail, passed the Lieutenant without speaking, snatched the keys from a nail on the wall, and removed from a cell one of her students who had been jailed after a drunken spree. The officer tried to stand in her way, but she shoved him aside and marched the boy outside by the back of his collar. Once in the street, she had given him a couple of smacks and assured him that the next time this happened she would lower his pants and give him a spanking he would never forget. The day that Ines came to tell Riad Halabi she had killed one of her clients, he did not doubt for a moment that she was serious, because he knew her too well. He took her arm and walked with her the two blocks that separated The Pearl of the Orient from her house. It was one of the grandest buildings in town, adobe and wood, with a wide veranda where hammocks were hung during the hottest siestas, and ceiling fans in every room. At that hour the house seemed to be empty; only one guest sat in the parlour drinking beer, mesmerized by the television.

'Where is he?' whispered the Arab merchant.

'In one of the back rooms,' Ines replied, not even lowering her voice.

She led him to the row of rooms she rented – all joined by an arcade with purple morning glories climbing the columns and pots of ferns hanging from the beams – bordering a patio planted with medlar and banana trees. Ines opened the last door and Riad Halabi entered a room in deep shadow. The shutters were closed, and it was a moment before he saw on the bed the corpse of an inoffensive-looking old man, a decrepit stranger swimming in the puddle of his own death, his trousers stained with excrement, his head hanging by a strip of ashen flesh, and wearing a terrible expression of distress, as if apologizing for all the disturbance and blood, and for the uncommon bother of having allowed himself to be murdered. Riad Halabi sat down on the room's only chair, his eyes on the floor, trying to control the lurch of his stomach. Ines remained standing, arms across her chest, calculating that it would take her two days to wash out the stains and at least two more to rid the room of its odour of faeces and fear.

'How did you do it?' Riad Halabi asked finally, wiping the sweat from his forehead.

'With the machete for harvesting coconuts. I came up behind him and lopped off his head with one swing. He never knew what hit him, poor man.'

'Why?'

'I had to do it. It was fate. This old man had very bad luck. He never meant to stop in Agua Santa; he was driving through town and a rock shattered his windshield. He came to pass a few hours here while the Italian down at the garage found another windshield. He's changed a lot – we've all grown older, I guess but I recognized him instantly. I've been waiting all these years; I knew he would come sooner or later. He's the man with the mangoes.'

'May Allah protect us,' murmured Riad Halabi.

'Do you think we should call the Lieutenant?'

'Not on your life; why do you say that?'

'I'm in the right, he killed my boy.'

'The Lieutenant wouldn't understand that, Ines.'

'An eye for an eye and a tooth for a tooth, Turk. Isn't that what your religion teaches?'

'But that's not how the law works, Ines.'

'Well, then, we can fix him up a little and say he committed suicide.'

'Don't touch him. How many guests do you have in the house?'

'Just that truckdriver. He'll be on his way as soon as it's cool; he had to drive to the capital.'

'Good. Don't take in any more guests. Lock the door to this room and wait for me. I'll be back tonight.'

'What are you going to do?'

'I'll take care of this in my own way.'

Riad Halabi was sixty-five years old, but he had conserved his youthful vigour and the same spirit that had positioned him at the head of the throng the day he arrived in Agua Santa. He left the schoolteacher's house and walked rapidly to the first of several visits he was to make that afternoon. Soon after, a persistent murmur began to spread through the town. The inhabitants of Agua Santa wakened from the lethargy of years, excited by the unbelievable news that was being repeated from house to house, an insuppressible buzzing, information that strained to be uttered in shouts, gossip that by the very need to be held to a murmur was conferred special status. Before sunset you could sense in the air the restless elation that for several years would be a characteristic of the town, one incomprehensible to strangers passing through, who could find nothing extraordinary in this town which had the appearance of being an insignificant backwater like so many others on the edge of the jungle. Early in the evening, men began arriving at the tavern; women carried their kitchen chairs out to the sidewalk and sat down to enjoy the cool air; young people gathered en masse in the plaza, as if it were Sunday. The Lieutenant and his men casually made their rounds and then accepted the invitation of the girls at the whorehouse who were celebrating a birthday, they said. By nightfall there were more people in the street than on All Saints' Day; all of them were so studiously occupied in their activities that they seemed to be practising a part in a movie: some were playing dominoes, other were drinking rum and smoking on the street corners, some couples were out for a stroll, hand in hand, mothers were running after their children, grandmothers peering nosily from open doorways. The priest lighted the lamps in the parish church and rang the bells signalling a novena to Saint Isidro Martyr, but no one was in the mood for that kind of devotion.

At nine-thirty there was a meeting in the house of schoolteacher Ines: the Turk, the town doctor, and four young men she had taught from the first grade and who were now hefty veterans back from military service. Riad Halabi led them to the back room, where they found the cadaver covered with insects: the window had been left open and it was the hour of the mosquitoes. They stuffed the victim in a canvas sack, wrestled it out to the street, and unceremoniously threw it into the back of Riad Halabi's truck. They drove through the town, right down the main street, waving, as usual, to anyone they happened to see. Some neighbours returned their salutation with more than ordinary enthusiasm, while others pretended not to notice them, furtively giggling, like children surprised at some mischief. Beneath brilliant moonlight the men drove to the spot where many years before the son of the schoolteacher Ines had stooped down for the last time to pick up a mango. The overgrown property sat amid the malign weeds of neglect, decayed by time and bad memories, a tangled hill where mangoes had grown wild, where fruit had dropped from the trees and taken root in the ground, giving birth to new clumps that had in turn engendered others, until an impenetrable jungle had been created that had swallowed up fences, path, even the ruins of the house, of which only a lingering trace of the odour of marmalade remained. The men lighted their kerosene lanterns and plunged into the dense growth, hacking a path with their machetes. When they felt they had gone far enough, one of them pointed to a spot and there, at the foot of a gigantic tree weighed down with fruit, they dug a deep hole in which they deposited the canvas sack. Before shovelling back the dirt, Riad Halabi spoke a brief Muslim prayer, because he knew no other. When they got back to town at midnight, they found that no one had gone to bed; lights were blazing in every window, and people were circulating through the streets.

Meanwhile, the schoolteacher Ines had scrubbed the walls and furniture in the back room with soap and water; she had burned the bedclothing, aired the house, and was waiting for her friends with a fine dinner and a pitcher of rum and pineapple juice. The meal was eaten to the accompaniment of merry chatter about the latest cockfights – a barbaric sport according to the schoolteacher, but less barbaric, the men alleged, than the bullfights in which a Colombian matador had just lost his liver. Riad Halabi was the last to say goodbye. That night, for the first time in his life, he felt old. At the door, the schoolteacher Ines took his hands and for a moment held them in hers.

'Thank you, Turk,' she said.

'Why did you come to me, Ines?'

'Because you are the person I love most in this world, and because you should have been the father of my son.'

The next day the inhabitants of Agua Santa returned to their usual chores exalted by a magnificent complicity, by a secret kept by good neighbours, one they would guard with absolute zeal and pass down for many years as a legend of justice, until the death of the schoolteacher Ines freed us, and now I can tell the story.

Isabel Allende

Working on
The Schoolteacher's Guest

_____ *Before reading* _____

1. The first sentence
● Read the first sentence of the story.

'The Schoolteacher Ines entered The Pearl of the Orient, deserted at this hour, walked to the counter where Riad Halabi was rolling up a bolt of bright-flowered cloth, and announced to him that she had just cut off the head of a guest in her boarding house.'

● Talk about these issues:

– what do you think might have happened to cause this situation?
– what effect does this opening have on you as a reader?

● Each write your own second paragraph for the story, then share them as a class before reading on.

_____ *After reading* _____

2. Then and now
The story starts with the news of the killing of the guest. We hear what happens next, but also what happened in the past.
● Use a chart like the one below to help you to sort out chronologically the history of Ines and Riad Halabi and the events of the story.

Then	Now
1. Ines' son was killed the day that Riad Halabi arrived in town. He helped with the funeral	1. Ines kills the guest at her boarding house

3. The ending
Look at the end of the story, from 'Meanwhile, the schoolteacher Ines had scrubbed the walls......'

● What new ideas and information does the ending give you about:

– Ines?
– Riad Halabi?
– the narrator?
– the attitude of the town to the events of the story?

4. Ines and the townspeople

We are given a lot of information about the townspeople and their attitude to Ines.
● Find two or three quotes from different times in the story that show how they feel about her (from the time of the death of the boy, from the time of her teaching, from the time of the guest house and from the time after the death of the guest).

5. Mangoes

● Look through the story for each time mangoes feature in the events or in the telling of the story.

– Why are they so important?
– Why do you think the writer keeps bringing them back into the story?
– What style of writing does the writer adopt when she talks about the mangoes?

6. What kind of story?

● Look at the list of words below. They are all different words for 'story'. Try to define each one. Use a dictionary to help you.
● Talk about which you think is most suitable for 'The Schoolteacher's Guest' and why.

– story
– legend
– history
– ballad
– tale
– anecdote
– myth
– romance

7. Magical realism

Isobel Allende has been linked with a group of Latin American writers called 'magical realists'. The name suggests that their stories are both mysterious or magical and true to life. Things happen that are not completely realistic but the writer presents them in a way that seems real.
● Find three or four events, descriptions, or images in the story that are mysterious or bizarre, larger than life or magical. Talk about what makes them strange, but also how the writer makes us believe in them.
● From your reading of 'The Schoolteacher's Guest', do you think 'magical realist' is a good way of describing the story?

8. Other voices

The narrative is told from a distance by one of the townspeople, so one never enters into the thoughts and feelings of Ines or Riad Halabi except from afar.
● Try re-writing the story from the point of view of one of these characters, to explore what difference it makes to hear the events in the voice of a participant.

9. Comparative work – communities and individuals

'A Basket Full of Wallpaper', 'Joebell and America', 'Mrs Turner Cutting the Grass' and 'American Dreams' are other stories which show individuals and the communities in which they live.
● Compare the ways in which two or more of these stories present the individual and the community. You might want to consider:

– what is the relationship of the individual to the community in each story?
– what is similar/different about the individuals and the communities in the stories?
– how does each writer create the community for the reader?
– what does each writer seem to be saying about what communities can be like?
– what themes or ideas do the stories throw up?

10. Comparative work – the death of a child

Look at the suggestions for comparative work after the short story, 'A Small Good Thing'.

11. Wider reading

● This story comes from a collection by Isobel Allende called *The Stories of Eva Luna*, which deals with love, violence, betrayal, death and mystery in a Latin American setting.
● Allende's novel, *The House of Spirits*, is a magical, highly dramatic story of three generations of a family living in an unnamed Latin American country.
● Gabriel Garcia Marquez's collection of short stories, *No-one Writes to the Colonel*, would make an interesting comparison with Allende's short stories, as they have a similar setting and both have elements of magical realism.
● 'Vendetta' by Guy de Maupassant is set in Sardinia in the last century. It tells the story of a mother's revenge for the death of her son.

American Dreams

No one can, to this day, remember what it was we did to offend him. Dyer the butcher remembers a day when he gave him the wrong meat and another day when he served someone else first by mistake. Often when Dyer gets drunk he recalls this day and curses himself for his foolishness. But no one seriously believes that it was Dyer who offended him.

But one of us did something. We slighted him terribly in some way, this small meek man with the rimless glasses and neat suit who used to smile so nicely at us all. We thought, I suppose, he was a bit of a fool and sometimes he was so quiet and grey that we ignored him, forgetting he was there at all.

When I was a boy I often stole apples from the trees at his house up in Mason's Lane. He often saw me. No, that's not correct. Let me say I often sensed that he saw me. I sensed him peering out from behind the lace curtains of his house. And I was not the only one. Many of us came to take his apples, alone and in groups, and it is possible that he chose to exact payment for all these apples in his own peculiar way.

Yet I am sure it wasn't the apples.

What has happened is that we all, all eight hundred of us, have come to remember small transgressions against Mr Gleason who once lived amongst us.

My father, who has never borne malice against a single living creature, still believes that Gleason meant to do us well, that he loved the town more than any of us. My father says we have treated the town badly in our minds. We have used it, this little valley, as nothing more than a stopping place. Somewhere on the way to somewhere else. Even those of us who have been here many years have never taken the town seriously. Oh yes, the place is pretty. The hills are green and the woods thick. The stream is full of fish. But it is not where we would rather be.

For years we have watched the films at the Roxy and dreamed, if not of America, then at least of our capital city. For our own town, my father says, we have nothing but contempt. We have treated it badly, like a whore. We have cut down the giant shady trees in the main street to make doors for the school house and seats for the football pavilion. We have left big holes all over the countryside from which we have taken brown coal and given back nothing.

The commercial travellers who buy fish and chips at George the Greek's care for us more than we do, because we all have dreams of the big city, of wealth, of modern houses, of big motor cars: American Dreams, my father has called them.

Although my father ran a petrol station he was also an inventor. He sat in his office all day drawing strange pieces of equipment on the back of delivery dockets. Every spare piece of paper in the house was covered with these little drawings and my mother would always be very careful about throwing away any piece of paper no matter how small. She would look on both sides of any piece of paper very carefully and always preserved any that had so much as a pencil mark.

I think it was because of this that my father felt that he understood Gleason. He never said as much, but he inferred that he understood Gleason because he, too, was concerned with similar problems. My father was working on plans for a giant gravel crusher, but occasionally he would become distracted and become interested in something else.

There was, for instance, the time when Dyer the butcher bought a new bicycle with gears, and for a while my father talked of nothing else but the gears. Often I would see him across the road squatting down beside Dyer's bicycle as if he were talking to it.

We all rode bicycles because we didn't have the money for anything better. My father did have an old Chev truck, but he rarely used it and it occurs to me now that it might have had some mechanical problem that was impossible to solve, or perhaps it was just that he was saving it, not wishing to wear it out all at once. Normally, he went everywhere on his bicycle and, when I was younger, he carried me on the cross bar, both of us dismounting to trudge up the hills that led into and out of the main street. It was a common sight in our town to see people pushing bicycles. They were as much a burden as a means of transport.

Gleason also had his bicycle and every lunchtime he pushed and pedalled it home from the shire offices to his little weatherboard house out at Mason's Lane. It was a three-mile ride and people said that he went home for lunch because he was fussy and wouldn't eat either his wife's sandwiches or the hot meal available at Mrs Lessing's café.

But while Gleason pedalled and pushed his bicycle to and from the shire offices everything in our town proceeded as normal. It was only when he retired that things began to go wrong.

Because it was then that Mr Gleason started supervising the building of the wall around the two-acre plot up on Bald Hill. He paid too much for this land. He bought it from Johnny Weeks, who now, I am sure, believes the whole episode was his fault, firstly for cheating Gleason, secondly for selling him the land at all. But Gleason hired some Chinese and set to work to build his wall. It was then that we knew that we'd offended him. My father rode all the way out to Bald Hill and tried to talk Mr Gleason out of his wall. He said there was no need for us to build walls. That no one wished to spy on Mr Gleason or whatever he wished to do on Bald Hill. He said no one was in the least bit interested in Mr Gleason. Mr Gleason, neat in a new sportscoat, polished his glasses and smiled vaguely at his feet. Bicycling back, my father thought that he had gone too far. Of course we had an interest in Mr Gleason. He pedalled back and asked him to attend a dance that was to be held on the next Friday, but Mr Gleason said he didn't dance.

'Oh well,' my father said, 'any time, just drop over.'

Mr Gleason went back to supervising his family of Chinese labourers on his wall.

Bald Hill towered high above the town and from my father's small filling station you could sit and watch the wall going up. It was an interesting sight. I watched it for two years, while I waited for customers who rarely came. After school and on Saturdays I had all the time in the world to watch the agonizing progress of Mr Gleason's wall. It was as painful as a clock. Sometimes I could see the Chinese labourers running at a jog-trot carrying bricks on long wooden planks. The hill was bare, and on this bareness Mr Gleason was, for some reason, building a wall.

In the beginning people thought it peculiar that someone would build such a big wall on Bald Hill. The only thing to recommend Bald Hill was the view of the town, and Mr Gleason was building a wall that denied that view. The top soil was thin and bare clay showed through in places. Nothing would ever grow there. Everyone assumed that Gleason had simply gone mad and after the initial interest they accepted his madness as they accepted his wall and as they accepted Bald Hill itself.

Occasionally someone would pull in for petrol at my father's filling station and ask about the wall and my father would shrug and I would see, once more, the strangeness of it.

'A house?' the stranger would ask. 'Up on that hill?'

'No,' my father would say, 'chap named Gleason is building a wall.'

And the strangers would want to know why, and my father would shrug and look up at Bald Hill once more. 'Damned if I know,' he'd say.

Gleason still lived in his old house at Mason's Lane. It was a plain weatherboard house with a rose garden at the front, a vegetable garden down the side, and an orchard at the back.

At night we kids would sometimes ride out to Bald Hill on our bicycles. It was an agonizing, muscle-twitching ride, the worst part of which was a steep, unmade road up which we finally pushed our bikes, our lungs rasping in the night air. When we arrived we found nothing but walls. Once we broke down some of the brickwork and another time we threw stones at the tents where the Chinese labourers slept. Thus we expressed our frustration at this inexplicable thing.

The wall must have been finished on the day before my twelfth birthday. I remember going on a picnic birthday party up to Eleven Mile Creek and we lit a fire and cooked chops at a bend in the river from where it was possible to see the walls on Bald Hill. I remember standing with a hot chop in my hand and someone saying, 'Look, they're leaving!'

We stood on the creek bed and watched the Chinese labourers walking their bicycles slowly down the hill. Someone said they were going to build a chimney up at the mine at A.1 and certainly there is a large brick chimney there now, so I suppose they built it.

When the word spread that the walls were finished most of the town went up to look. They walked around the four walls which were as interesting as any other brick walls. They stood in front of the big wooden gates and tried to peer through, but all they could see was a small blind wall that had obviously been constructed for this special purpose. The walls themselves were ten feet high and topped with broken glass and barbed wire. When it became obvious that we were not going to discover the contents of the enclosure, we all gave up and went home.

Mr Gleason had long since stopped coming into town. His wife came instead, wheeling a pram down from Mason's Lane to Main Street and filling it with groceries and meat (they never bought vegetables, they grew their own) and wheeling it back to Mason's Lane. Sometimes you would see her standing with the pram halfway up the Gell Street hill. Just standing there, catching her breath. No one asked her about the wall. They knew she wasn't responsible for the wall and they felt sorry for her, having to bear the burden of the pram and her husband's madness. Even when she began to visit Dixon's hardware and buy plaster of paris and tins of paint and waterproofing compound, no one asked her what these things were for. She had a way of averting her eyes that indicated her terror of questions. Old Dixon carried the plaster of paris and the tins of paint out to her pram for her and watched her push them away. 'Poor woman,' he said, 'poor bloody woman.'

From the filling station where I sat dreaming in the sun, or from the enclosed office where I gazed mournfully at the rain, I would see, occasionally, Gleason entering or leaving his walled compound, a tiny figure way up on Bald Hill. And I'd think 'Gleason', but not much more.

Occasionally strangers drove up there to see what was going on, often egged on by locals who told them it was a Chinese temple or some other silly thing. Once a group of Italians had a picnic outside the walls and took photographs of each other standing in front of the closed door. God knows what they thought it was.

But for five years between my twelfth and seventeenth birthdays there was nothing to interest me in Gleason's walls. Those years seem lost to me now and I can remember very little of them. I developed a crush on Susy Markin and followed her back from the swimming pool on my bicycle. I sat behind her in the pictures and wandered past her house. Then her parents moved to another town and I sat in the sun and waited for them to come back.

We became very keen on modernization. When coloured paints became available the whole town went berserk and brightly coloured houses blossomed overnight. But the paints were not of good quality and quickly faded and peeled, so that the town looked like a garden of dead flowers. Thinking of those years, the only real thing I recall is the soft hiss of bicycle tyres on the main street. When I think of it now it seems very peaceful, but I remember then that the sound induced in me a feeling of melancholy, a feeling somehow mixed with the early afternoons when the sun went down behind Bald Hill and the town felt as sad as an empty dance hall on a Sunday afternoon.

And then, during my seventeenth year, Mr Gleason died. We found out when we saw Mrs Gleason's pram parked out in front of Phonsey Joy's Funeral Parlour. It looked very sad, that pram, standing by itself in the windswept street. We came and looked at the pram and felt sad for Mrs Gleason. She hadn't had much of a life.

Phonsey Joy carried old Mr Gleason out to the cemetery by the Parwan Railway Station and Mrs Gleason rode behind in a taxi. People watched the old hearse go by and thought, 'Gleason', but not much else.

And then, less than a month after Gleason had been buried out at the lonely cemetery by the Parwan Railway Station, the Chinese labourers came back. We saw them push their bicycles up the hill. I stood with my father and Phonsey Joy and wondered what was going on.

And then I saw Mrs Gleason trudging up the hill. I nearly didn't recognize her, because she didn't have her pram. She carried a black umbrella and walked slowly up Bald Hill and it wasn't until she stopped for breath and leant forward that I recognized her.

'It's Mrs Gleason,' I said, 'with the Chinese.'

But it wasn't until the next morning that it became obvious what was happening. People lined the main street in the way they do for a big funeral but, instead of gazing towards the Grant Street corner, they all looked up at Bald Hill.

All that day and all the next people gathered to watch the destruction of the walls. They saw the Chinese labourers darting to and fro, but it wasn't until they knocked down a large section of the wall facing the town that we realized there really was something inside. It was impossible to see what it was, but there was something there. People stood and wondered and pointed out Mrs Gleason to each other as she went to and fro supervising the work.

And finally, in ones and twos, on bicycles and on foot, the whole town moved up to Bald Hill. Mr Dyer closed up his butcher shop and my father got out the old Chev truck and we finally arrived up at Bald Hill with twenty people on board. They crowded into the back tray and hung on to the running boards and my father grimly steered his way through the crowds of bicycles and parked just where the dirt track gets really steep. We trudged up this last steep track, never for a moment suspecting what we would find at the top.

It was very quiet up there. The Chinese labourers worked diligently, removing the third and fourth walls and cleaning the bricks which they stacked neatly in big piles. Mrs Gleason said nothing either. She stood in the only remaining corner of the walls and looked defiantly at the townspeople who stood open-mouthed where another corner had been.

And between us and Mrs Gleason was the most incredibly beautiful thing I had ever seen in my life. For one moment I didn't recognize it. I stood open-mouthed, and breathed the surprising beauty of it. And then I realized it was our town. The buildings were two feet high and they were a little rough but very correct. I saw Mr Dyer nudge my father and whisper that Gleason had got the faded 'U' in the BUTCHER sign of his shop.

I think at that moment everyone was overcome with a feeling of simple joy. I can't remember ever having felt so uplifted and happy. It was perhaps a childish emotion but I looked up at my father and saw a smile of such warmth spread across his face that I knew he felt just as I did. Later he told me that he thought Gleason had built the model of our town just for this moment, to let us see the beauty of our own town, to make us proud of ourselves and to stop the American Dreams we were so prone to. For the rest, my father said, was not Gleason's plan and he could not have foreseen the things that happened afterwards.

I have come to think that this view of my father's is a little sentimental and also, perhaps, insulting to Gleason. I personally believe that he knew everything that would happen. One day the proof of my theory may be discovered. Certainly there are in existence some personal papers, and I firmly believe that these papers will show that Gleason knew exactly what would happen.

We had been so overcome by the model of the town that we hadn't noticed what was the most remarkable thing of all. Not only had Gleason built the houses and the shops of our town, he had also peopled it. As we tip-toed into the town we suddenly found ourselves. 'Look,' I said to Mr Dyer, 'there you are.'

And there he was, standing in front of his shop in his apron. As I bent down to examine the tiny figure I was staggered by the look on its face. The modelling was crude, the paintwork was sloppy, and the face a little too white, but the expression was absolutely perfect: those pursed, quizzical lips and the eyebrows lifted high. It was Mr Dyer and no one else on earth.

And there beside Mr Dyer was my father, squatting on the footpath and gazing lovingly at Mr Dyer's bicycle's gears, his face marked with grease and hope.

And there was I, back at the filling station, leaning against a petrol pump in an American pose and talking to Brian Sparrow who was amusing me with his clownish antics.

Phonsey Joy standing beside his hearse. Mr Dixon sitting inside his hardware store. Everyone I knew was there in that tiny town. If they were not in the streets or in their backyards they were inside their houses, and it didn't take very long to discover that you could lift off the roofs and peer inside.

We tip-toed around the streets peeping into each other's windows, lifting off each other's roofs, admiring each other's gardens, and, while we did it, Mrs Gleason slipped silently away down the hill towards Mason's Lane. She spoke to nobody and nobody spoke to her.

I confess that I was the one who took the roof from Cavanagh's house. So I was the one who found Mrs Cavanagh in bed with young Craigie Evans.

I stood there for a long time, hardly knowing what I was seeing. I stared at the pair of them for a long, long time. And when I finally knew what I was seeing I felt such an incredible mixture of jealousy and guilt and wonder that I didn't know what to do with the roof.

Eventually it was Phonsey Joy who took the roof from my hands and placed it carefully back on the house, much, I imagine, as he would have placed the lid on a coffin. By then other people had seen what I had seen and the word passed around very quickly.

And then we all stood around in little groups and regarded the model town with what could only have been fear. If Gleason knew about Mrs Cavanagh and Craigie Evans (and no one else had), what other things might he know? Those who hadn't seen themselves yet in the town began to look a little nervous and were unsure of whether to look for themselves or not. We gazed silently at the roofs and felt mistrustful and guilty.

We all walked down the hill then, very quietly, the way people walk away from a funeral, listening only to the crunch of the gravel under our feet while the women had trouble with their high-heeled shoes.

The next day a special meeting of the shire council passed a motion calling on Mrs Gleason to destroy the model town on the grounds that it contravened building regulations.

It is unfortunate that this order wasn't carried out before the city newspapers found out. Before another day had gone by the government had stepped in.

The model town and its model occupants were to be preserved. The minister for tourism came in a large black car and made a speech to us in the football pavilion. We sat on the high, tiered seats eating potato chips while he stood against the fence and talked to us. We couldn't hear him very well, but we heard enough. He called the model town a work of art and we stared at him grimly. He said it would be an invaluable tourist attraction. He said tourists would come from everywhere to see the model town. We would be famous. Our businesses would flourish. There would be work for guides and interpreters and caretakers and taxi drivers and people selling soft drinks and ice creams.

The Americans would come, he said. They would visit our town in buses and in cars and on the train. They would take photographs and bring wallets bulging with dollars. American dollars.

We looked at the minister mistrustfully, wondering if he knew about Mrs Cavanagh, and he must have seen the look because he said that certain controversial items would be removed, had already been removed. We shifted in our seats, like you do when a particularly tense part of a film has come to its climax, and then we relaxed and listened to what the minister had to say. And we all began, once more, to dream our American Dreams.

We saw our big smooth cars cruising through cities with bright lights. We entered expensive night clubs and danced till dawn. We made love to women like Kim Novak and men like Rock Hudson. We drank cocktails. We gazed lazily into refrigerators filled with food and prepared ourselves lavish midnight snacks which we ate while we watched huge television sets on which we would be able to see American movies free of charge and forever.

The minister, like someone from our American Dreams, re-entered his large black car and cruised slowly from our humble sportsground, and the newspaper men arrived and swarmed over the pavilion with their cameras and notebooks. They took photographs of us and photographs of the models up on Bald Hill. And the next day we were all over the newspapers. The photographs of the model people side by side with photographs of the real people. And our names and ages and what we did were all printed there in black and white.

They interviewed Mrs Gleason but she said nothing of interest. She said the model town had been her husband's hobby.

We all felt good now. It was very pleasant to have your photograph in the paper. And, once more, we changed our opinion of Gleason. The shire council held another meeting and named the dirt track up Bald Hill, 'Gleason Avenue'. Then we all went home and waited for the Americans we had been promised.

It didn't take long for them to come, although at the time it seemed an eternity, and we spent six long months doing nothing more with our lives than waiting for the Americans.

Well, they did come. And let me tell you how it has all worked out for us.

The Americans arrive every day in buses and cars and sometimes the younger ones come on the train. There is now a small airstrip out near the Parwan cemetery and they also arrive there, in small aeroplanes. Phonsey Joy drives them to the cemetery where they look at Gleason's grave and then up to Bald Hill and then down to the town. He is doing very well from it all. It is good to see someone doing well from it. Phonsey is becoming a big man in town and is on the shire council.

On Bald Hill there are half a dozen telescopes through which the Americans can spy on the town and reassure themselves that it is the same down there as it is on Bald Hill. Herb Gravney sells them ice creams and soft drinks and extra film for their cameras. He is another one who is doing well. He bought the whole model from Mrs Gleason and charges five American dollars admission. Herb is on the council now too. He's doing very well for himself. He sells them the film so they can take photographs of the houses and the model people and so they can come down to the town with their special maps and hunt out the real people.

To tell the truth most of us are pretty sick of the game. They come looking for my father and ask him to stare at the gears of Dyer's bicycle. I watch my father cross the street slowly, his head hung low. He doesn't greet the Americans any more. He doesn't ask them questions about colour television or Washington D.C. He kneels on the footpath in front of Dyer's bike. They stand around him. Often they remember the model incorrectly and try to get my father to pose in the wrong way. Originally he argued with them, but now he argues no more. He does what they ask. They push him this way and that and worry about the expression on his face which is no longer what it was.

Then I know they will come to find me. I am next on the map. I am very popular for some reason. They come in search of me and my petrol pump as they have done for four years now. I do not await them eagerly because I know, before they reach me, that they will be disappointed.

'But this is not the boy.'

'Yes,' says Phonsey, 'this is him alright.' And he gets me to show them my certificate.

They examine the certificate suspiciously, feeling the paper as if it might be a clever forgery. 'No,' they declare. (Americans are so confident.) 'No,' they shake their heads, 'this is not the real boy. The real boy is younger.'

'He's older now. He used to be younger.' Phonsey looks weary when he tells them. He can afford to look weary.

The Americans peer at my face closely. 'It's a different boy.'

But finally they get their cameras out. I stand sullenly and try to look amused as I did once. Gleason saw me looking amused but I can no longer remember how it felt. I was looking at Brian Sparrow. But Brian is also tired. He finds it difficult to do his clownish antics and to the Americans his little act isn't funny. They prefer the model. I watch him sadly, sorry that he must perform for such an unsympathetic audience.

The Americans pay one dollar for the right to take our photographs. Having paid the money they are worried about being cheated. They spend their time being disappointed and I spend my time feeling guilty that I have somehow let them down by growing older and sadder.

Peter Carey

Working on American Dreams

1. The title
● Brainstorm your ideas, associations and expectations around the title 'American Dreams.'

2. Reading the story: stage 1
● Stop reading on page 18 where it says: 'It was only when he retired that things began to go wrong.'
● In small groups discuss and make notes about the following:

– the people in the town
– the places in the town
– events that have occurred
– ideas or issues raised so far in the story
– a phrase that struck you
– questions you would like to ask about this story
– what you think is going to happen next

3. Reading the story: stage 2
● Stop reading on page 21 where it says: 'We trudged up this last steep track, never for a moment suspecting what we would find at the top.'

What do you think is behind the wall? Share your ideas in small groups. Where possible show how your ideas are suggested by what has happened in the story so far.

● Try writing the next section of the story. You could just write the first paragraph or try the whole thing. Whatever you write, try to keep the characters, the places and the style of the narrator as close to Peter Carey's writing as you can.

4. Reading the story: stage 3
● Stop reading on page 24 where it says: 'Well, they did come. And let me tell you how it has all worked out for us.'

In this section, the reactions of the townspeople to what they find behind the wall are revealed. Their reactions are mixed and change as they see the implications of what Mr Gleason has done.

- Collect some quotes to show the reactions and implications of what the townspeople see, and present them in a chart like the one below:

Positive	Negative
1. 'the most incredibly beautiful thing I had ever seen in my life'	'We gazed silently at the roofs and felt mistrustful and guilty.'

- Talk about your own reactions to what Mr Gleason has done. Has he done them a favour or is what he's done an act of spite?

5. Reading the story: stage 4
- Read the final section of the story in which we are told what life is like for the townspeople once the Americans arrive. Talk about your reactions to this section.

– why do the Americans come?
– how are the townspeople affected by their visit?
– is this what they hoped for when they dreamed of the Americans coming?

--- *After reading* ---

6. The town
The story is set in a town in Australia.
- What kind of a place is the town before the Americans come?
- Make a plan or diagram of the town. Put some of the characters into the plan with short quotes and comments to show the kind of people they are and the sorts of things they do and think.

7. The characters
- Take some of the following characters and think about their place in the story. What role do they play? What do you think they stand for or represent?

– the narrator
– the narrator's father
– Dyer
– Phonsey Joy
– Gleason
– Mrs Gleason

8. Mr Gleason
Mr Gleason is a key character in this story, but we don't know much about him.
- In small groups discuss everything you do know about him and speculate on why he built the wall.

9. What is this story about?

● Here are various suggestions of what the story is about. Talk about whether you agree with them or not, and add one of your own.

The importance of community in people's lives
The impatience of youth
The suffocating nature of small towns
Every town has its secrets
The destructive nature of gossip
The death of a town from tourism
The corrupting nature of American values
The folly of wishing your life away
People's blindness to what they have in life
An isolated man's revenge

10. Comparative work – isolated individuals

'A Basket Full of Wallpaper' is another story about a community and its relationship with one rather unusual individual who has an unknown past and an unknown motive for what he does.

● Compare the ways in which each of the writers presents this relationship and the themes that are explored along the way. You might want to focus on similarities and differences in the stories by looking at:

– who the narrator is and the voice in which he tells the story
– how dialogue is used to reveal the nature of the community, the narrator's position within it and the way the individual is seen
– the key moments in each story and what their purpose seems to be
– the tone of each story (sad, nostalgic, funny, bitter?)
– what themes are being explored and in what ways?

● Write an imaginative piece in which Mr Gleason and Osobe meet and reveal more about themselves to each other.

11. Comparative work – American dreams

Look at the suggestions for comparative work after the short story, 'Joebell and America'.

12. Comparative work – other worlds

Look at the suggestions for comparative work after the short story, 'Headless'.

13. Comparative work – communities and individuals

Look at the suggestions for comparative work after the short story, 'The Schoolteacher's Guest'.

14. Wider reading

● This short story comes from a collection called *The Fat Man in History*, containing other original and unusual short stories.

● Janette Turner Hospital is a contemporary Australian short story writer. Her collection of stories, *Isobars*, has been published by Virago. 'The Second Coming of Come-by-Chance' is a story about a town long submerged by water, which re-surfaces in a drought, revealing the secrets of one woman's past.

● *Shirley Valentine* by Willy Russell is a play about a woman's dream of escape from her dull routine life. A holiday on a Greek island makes this dream suddenly seem like a reality.

● Thomas Hardy's *Wessex Tales* create a strong sense of communities. Individual dramas are played out against a background of local interest and comment, and strange events are presented.

A Small
Good Thing

Saturday afternoon she drove to the bakery in the shopping center. After looking through a loose-leaf binder with photographs of cakes taped onto the pages, she ordered chocolate, the child's favourite. The cake she chose was decorated with a space ship and launching pad under a sprinkling of white stars, and a planet made of red frosting at the other end. His name, SCOTTY, would be in green letters beneath the planet. The baker, who was an older man with a thick neck, listened without saying anything when she told him the child would be eight years old next Monday. The baker wore a white apron that looked like a smock. Straps cut under his arms, went around in back and then to the front again, where they were secured under his heavy waist. He wiped his hands on his apron as he listened to her. He kept his eyes down on the photographs and let her talk. He let her take her time. He'd just come to work and he'd be there all night, baking, and he was in no real hurry.

She gave the baker her name, Ann Weiss, and her telephone number. The cake would be ready on Monday morning, just out of the oven, in plenty of time for the child's party that afternoon. The baker was not jolly. There were no pleasantries between them, just the minimum exchange of words, the necessary information. He made her feel uncomfortable, and she didn't like that. While he was bent over the counter with the pencil in his hand, she studied his coarse features and wondered if he'd ever done anything else with his life besides be a baker. She was a mother and thirty-three years old, and it seemed to her that everyone, especially someone the baker's age – a man old enough to be her father – must have children who'd gone through this special time of cakes and birthday parties. There must be that between them, she thought. But he was abrupt with her– not rude, just abrupt. She gave up trying to make friends with him. She looked into the back of the bakery and could see a long, heavy wooden table with aluminum pie pans stacked at one end; and beside the table a metal container filled with empty racks. There was an enormous oven. A radio was playing country-western music.

The baker finished printing the information on the special order card and closed up the binder. He looked at her and said, 'Monday morning.' She thanked him and drove home.

On Monday morning, the birthday boy was walking to school with another boy. They were passing a bag of potato chips back and forth and the birthday boy was trying to find out what his friend intended to give him for his birthday that afternoon. Without looking, the birthday boy stepped off the curb at an intersection and was immediately knocked down by a car. He fell on his side with his head in the gutter and his legs out in the road. His eyes were closed, but his legs moved back and forth as if he were trying to climb over something. His friend dropped the potato chips and started to cry. The car had gone a hundred feet or so and stopped in the middle of the road. The man in the driver's seat looked back over his shoulder. He waited until the boy got unsteadily to his feet. The boy wobbled a little. He looked dazed, but okay. The driver put the car into gear and drove away.

The birthday boy didn't cry, but he didn't have anything to say about anything either. He wouldn't answer when his friend asked him what it felt like to be hit by a car. He walked home, and his friend went on to school. But after the birthday boy was inside his house and was telling his mother about it – she sitting beside him on the sofa, holding his hands in her lap, saying, 'Scotty, honey, are you sure you feel all right, baby?' thinking she would call the doctor anyway – he suddenly lay back on the sofa, closed his eyes, and went limp. When she couldn't wake him up, she hurried to the telephone and called her husband at work. Howard told her to remain calm, and then he called an ambulance for the child and left for the hospital himself.

Of course, the birthday party was canceled. The child was in the hospital with a mild concussion and suffering from shock. There'd been vomiting, and his lungs had taken in fluid which needed pumping out that afternoon. Now he simply seemed to be in a very deep sleep – but no coma, Dr Francis had emphasized, no coma, when he saw the alarm in the parents' eyes. At eleven o'clock that night, when the boy seemed to be resting comfortably enough after the many X-rays and the lab work, and it was just a matter of his waking up and coming around, Howard left the hospital. He and Ann had been at the hospital with the child since that afternoon, and he was going home for a short while to bathe and change clothes. 'I'll be back in an hour,' he said. She nodded. 'It's fine,' she said. 'I'll be right here.' He kissed her on the forehead, and they touched hands. She sat in the chair beside the bed and looked at the child. She was waiting for him to wake up and be all right. Then she could begin to relax.

Howard drove home from the hospital. He took the wet, dark streets very fast, then caught himself and slowed down. Until now, his life had gone smoothly and to his satisfaction – college, marriage, another year of college for the advanced degree in business, a junior partnership in an investment firm. Fatherhood. He was happy and, so far, lucky – he knew that. His parents were still living, his brothers and his sister were established, his friends from college had gone out to take their places in the world. So far, he had kept away from any real harm, from those forces he knew existed and that could cripple or bring down a man if the luck went bad, if things suddenly turned. He pulled into the driveway and parked. His left leg began to tremble. He sat in the car for a minute and tried to deal with the present situation in a rational manner. Scotty had been hit by a car and was in the hospital, but he was going to be all right: Howard closed his eyes and ran his hand over his face. He got out of the car and went up to the front door. The dog was barking inside the house. The telephone rang and rang while he unlocked the door and fumbled for the light switch. He shouldn't have left the hospital, he shouldn't have. 'Goddamn it!' he said. He picked up the receiver and said, 'I just walked in the door!'

'There's a cake here that wasn't picked up,' the voice on the other end of the line said.

'What are you saying?' Howard asked.

'A cake,' the voice said. 'A sixteen-dollar cake.'

Howard held the receiver against his ear, trying to understand. 'I don't know anything about a cake,' he said. 'Jesus, what are you talking about?'

'Don't hand me that,' the voice said.

Howard hung up the telephone. He went into the kitchen and poured himself some whiskey. He called the hospital. But the child's condition remained the same; he was still sleeping and nothing had changed there. While water poured into the tub, Howard lathered his face and shaved. He'd just stretched out in the tub and closed his eyes when the telephone rang again. He hauled himself out, grabbed a towel, and hurried through the house, saying, 'Stupid, stupid,' for having left the hospital. But when he picked up the receiver and shouted, 'Hello!' there was no sound at the other end of the line. Then the caller hung up.

He arrived back at the hospital a little after midnight. Ann still sat in the chair beside the bed. She looked up at Howard, and then she looked back at the child. The child's eyes stayed closed, the head was still wrapped in bandages. His breathing was quiet and regular. From an apparatus over the bed hung a bottle of glucose with a tube running from the bottle to the boy's arm.

'How is he?' Howard said. 'What's all this?' waving at the glucose and the tube.

'Dr Francis's orders,' she said. 'He needs nourishment. He needs to keep up his strength. Why doesn't he wake up, Howard? I don't understand, if he's all right.'

Howard put his hand against the back of her head. He ran his fingers through her hair. 'He's going to be all right. He'll wake up in a little while. Dr Francis knows what's what.'

After a time, he said, 'Maybe you should go home and get some rest. I'll stay here. Just don't put up with this creep who keeps calling. Hang up right away.'

'Who's calling?' she asked.

'I don't know who, just somebody with nothing better to do than call up people. You go on now.'

She shook her head. 'No,' she said, 'I'm fine.'

'Really,' he said. 'Go home for a while, and then come back and spell me in the morning. It'll be all right. What did Dr Francis say? He said Scotty's going to be all right. We don't have to worry. He's just sleeping now, that's all.'

A nurse pushed the door open. She nodded at them as she went to the bedside. She took the left arm out from under the covers and put her fingers on the wrist, found the pulse, then consulted her watch. In a little while, she put the arm back under the covers and moved to the foot of the bed, where she wrote something on a clipboard attached to the bed.

'How is he?' Ann said. Howard's hand was a weight on her shoulder. She was aware of the pressure from his fingers.

'He's stable,' the nurse said. Then she said, 'Doctor will be in again shortly. Doctor's back in the hospital. He's making rounds right now.'

'I was saying maybe she'd want to go home and get a little rest,' Howard said. 'After the doctor comes,' he said.

'She could do that,' the nurse said. 'I think you should both feel free to do that, if you wish.' The nurse was a big Scandinavian woman with blond hair. There was the trace of an accent in her speech.

'We'll see what the doctor says,' Ann said. 'I want to talk to the doctor. I don't think he should keep sleeping like this. I don't think that's a good sign.' She brought her hand up to her eyes and let her head come forward a little. Howard's grip tightened on her shoulder, and then his hand moved up to her neck, where his fingers began to knead the muscles there.

'Dr Francis will be here in a few minutes,' the nurse said. Then she left the room.

Howard gazed at his son for a time, the small chest quietly rising and falling under the covers. For the first time since the terrible minutes after Ann's telephone call to him at his office, he felt a genuine fear starting in his limbs. He began shaking his head. Scotty was fine, but instead of sleeping at home in his own bed, he was in a hospital bed with bandages around his head and a tube in his arm. But this help was what he needed right now.

Dr Francis came in and shook hands with Howard, though they'd just seen each other a few hours before. Ann got up from the chair. 'Doctor?'

'Ann,' he said and nodded. 'Let's just first see how he's doing,' the doctor said. He moved to the side of the bed and took the boy's pulse. He peeled back one eyelid and then the other. Howard and Ann stood beside the doctor and watched. Then the doctor turned back the covers and listened to the boy's heart and lungs with his stethoscope. He pressed his fingers here and there on the abdomen. When he was finished, he went to the end of the bed and studied the chart. He noted the time, scribbled something on the chart, and then looked at Howard and Ann.

'Doctor, how is he?' Howard said. 'What's the matter with him exactly?'

'Why doesn't he wake up?' Ann said.

The doctor was handsome, big-shouldered man with a tanned face. He wore a three-piece blue suit, a striped tie, and ivory cufflinks. His gray hair was combed along the sides of his head, and he looked as if he had just come from a concert. 'He's all right,' the doctor said. 'Nothing to shout about, he could be better, I think. But he's all right. Still, I wish he'd wake up. He should wake up pretty soon.' The doctor looked at the boy again. 'We'll know some more in a couple of hours after the results of a few more tests are in. But he's all right, believe me, except for the hairline fracture of the skull. He does have that.'

'Oh, no,' Ann said.

'And a bit of a concussion, as I said before. Of course, you know he's in shock,' the doctor said. 'Sometimes you see this in shock cases. This sleeping.'

'But he's out of any real danger?' Howard said. 'You said before he's not in a coma. You wouldn't call this a coma, then – would you, doctor?' Howard waited. He looked at the doctor.

'No, I don't want to call it a coma,' the doctor said and glanced over at the boy once more. 'He's just in a very deep sleep. It's a restorative measure the body is taking on its own. He's out of any real danger, I'd say that for certain, yes. But we'll know more when he wakes up and the other tests are in,' the doctor said.

'It's a coma,' Ann said. 'Of sorts.'

'It's not a coma yet, not exactly,' the doctor said. 'I wouldn't want to call it coma. Not yet, anyway. He's suffered shock. In shock cases, this kind of reaction is common enough; it's, a temporary reaction to bodily trauma. Coma. Well, coma is a deep, prolonged unconsciousness, something that could go on for days, or weeks even. Scotty's not in that area, not as far as we can tell. I'm certain his condition will show improvement by morning. I'm betting that it will. We'll know more when he wakes up, which shouldn't be long now. Of course, you may do as you like, stay here or go home for a time. But by all means feel free to leave the hospital for a while if you want. This is not easy, I know.' The doctor gazed at the boy again, watching him, and then he turned to Ann and said, 'You try not to worry, little mother. Believe me, we're doing all that can be done. It's just a question of a little more time now.' He nodded at her, shook hands with Howard again, and then he left the room.

Ann put her hand over the child's forehead. 'At least he doesn't have a fever,' she said. Then she said, 'My God, he feels so cold, though. Howard? Is he supposed to feel like this? Feel his head.'

Howard touched the child's temples. His own breathing had slowed. 'I think he's supposed to feel this way right now,' he said. 'He's in shock, remember? That's what the doctor said. The doctor was just in here. He would have said something if Scotty wasn't okay.'

Ann stood there a while longer, working her lip with her teeth. Then she moved over to her chair and sat down.

Howard sat in the chair next to her chair. They looked at each other. He wanted to say something else and reassure her, but he was afraid, too. He took her hand and put it in his lap, and this made him feel better, her hand being there. He picked up her hand and squeezed it. Then he just held her hand. They sat like that for a while, watching the boy and not talking. From time to time, he squeezed her hand. Finally, she took her hand away.

'I've been praying,' she said.

He nodded.

She said, 'I almost thought I'd forgotten how, but it came back to me. All I had to do was close my eyes and say. 'Please God, help us – help Scotty,' and then the rest was easy. The words were right there. Maybe if you prayed, too,' she said to him.

'I've already prayed,' he said. 'I prayed this afternoon – yesterday afternoon, I mean – after you called, while I was driving to the hospital. I've been praying,' he said.

'That's good,' she said. For the first time, she felt they were together in it, this trouble. She realized with a start that, until now, it had only been happening to her and to Scotty. She hadn't let Howard into it, though he was there and needed all along. She felt glad to be his wife.

The same nurse came in and took the boy's pulse again and checked the flow from the bottle hanging above the bed.

In an hour, another doctor came in. He said his name was Parsons, from Radiology. He had a bushy mustache. He was wearing loafers, a Western shirt, and a pair of jeans.

'We're going to take him downstairs for more pictures,' he told them. 'We need to do some more pictures, and we want to do a scan.'

'What's that?' Ann said. 'A scan?' She stood between this new doctor and the bed. 'I thought you'd already taken all your X-rays.'

'I'm afraid we need some more,' he said. 'Nothing to be alarmed about. We just need some more pictures, and we want to do a brain scan on him.'

'My God,' Ann said.

'It's perfectly normal procedure in cases like this,' this new doctor said. 'We just need to find out for sure why he isn't back awake yet. It's normal medical procedure, and nothing to be alarmed about. We'll be taking him down in a few minutes,' this doctor said.

In a little while, two orderlies came into the room with a gurney. They were black-haired, dark-complexioned men in white uniforms, and they said a few words to each other in a foreign tongue as they unhooked the boy from the tube and moved him from his bed to the gurney. Then they wheeled him from the room. Howard and Ann got on the same elevator. Ann gazed at the child. She closed her eyes as the elevator began its descent. The orderlies stood at either end of the gurney without saying anything, though once one of the men made a comment to the other in their own language, and the other man nodded slowly in response.

Later that morning, just as the sun was beginning to lighten the windows in the waiting room outside the X-ray department, they brought the boy out and moved him back up to his room. Howard and Ann rode up on the elevator with him once more, and once more they took up their places beside the bed.

They waited all day, but still the boy did not wake up. Occasionally, one of them would leave the room to go downstairs to the cafeteria to drink coffee and then, as if suddenly remembering and feeling guilty, get up from the table and hurry back to the room. Dr Francis came again that afternoon and examined the boy once more and then left after telling them he was coming along and could wake up at any minute now. Nurses, different nurses from the night before, came in from time to time. Then a young woman from the lab knocked and entered the room. She wore white slacks and a white blouse and carried a little tray of things which she put on the stand beside the bed. Without a word to them, she took blood from the boy's arm. Howard closed his eyes as the woman found the right place on the boy's arm and pushed the needle in.

'I don't understand this,' Ann said to the woman.

'Doctor's orders,' the young woman said. 'I do what I'm told. They say draw that one, I draw. What's wrong with him, anyway?' she said. 'He's a sweetie.'

'He was hit by a car,' Howard said. 'A hit-and-run.'

The young woman shook her head and looked again at the boy. Then she took her tray and left the room.

'Why won't he wake up?' Ann said. 'Howard? I want some answers from these people.'

Howard didn't say anything. He sat down again in the chair and crossed one leg over the other. He rubbed his face. He looked at his son and then he settled back in the chair, closed his eyes, and went to sleep.

Ann walked to the window and looked out at the parking lot. It was night, and cars were driving into and out of the parking lot with their lights on. She stood at the window with her hands gripping the sill, and knew in her heart that they were into something now, something hard. She was afraid, and her teeth began to chatter until she tightened her jaws. She saw a big car stop in front of the hospital and someone, a woman in a long coat, get into the car. She wished she were that woman and somebody, anybody, was driving her away from here to somewhere else, a place where she would find Scotty waiting for her when she stepped out of the car, ready to say *Mom* and let her gather him in her arms.

In a little while, Howard woke up. He looked at the boy again. Then he got up from the chair, stretched, and went over to stand beside her at the window. They both stared out at the parking lot. They didn't say anything. But they seemed to feel each other's insides now, as though the worry had made them transparent in a perfectly natural way.

The door opened and Dr Francis came in. He was wearing a different suit and tie this time. His gray hair was combed along the sides of his head, and he looked as if he had just shaved. He went straight to the bed and examined the boy. 'He ought to have come around by now. There's just no good reason for this,' he said. 'But I can tell you we're all convinced he's out of any danger. We'll just feel better when he wakes up. There's no reason, absolutely none, why he shouldn't come around. Very soon. Oh, he'll have himself a dilly of a headache when he does, you can count on that. But all of his signs are fine. They're as normal as can be.'

'It is a coma, then?' Ann said.

The doctor rubbed his smooth cheek. 'We'll call it that for the time being, until he wakes up. But you must be worn out. This is hard. I know this is hard. Feel free to go out for a bite,' he said. 'It would do you good. I'll put a nurse in here while you're gone if you'll feel better about going. Go and have yourselves something to eat.'

'I couldn't eat anything,' Ann said.

'Do what you need to do, of course,' the doctor said.

'Anyway, I wanted to tell you that all the signs are good, the tests are negative, nothing showed up at all, and just as soon as he wakes up he'll be over the hill.'

'Thank you, doctor,' Howard said. He shook hands with the doctor again. The doctor patted Howard's shoulder and went out.

'I suppose one of us should go home and check on things,' Howard said. 'Slug needs to be fed, for one thing.'

'Call one of the neighbors,' Ann said. 'Call the Morgans. Anyone will feed a dog if you ask them to.'

'All right,' Howard said. After a while, he said, 'Honey, why don't you do it? Why don't you go home and check on things, and then come back? It'll do you good. I'll be right here with him. Seriously,' he said. 'We need to keep up our strength on this. We'll want to be here for a while even after he wakes up.'

'Why don't you go?' she said. 'Feed Slug. Feed yourself.'

'I already went,' he said. 'I was gone for exactly an hour and fifteen minutes. You go home for an hour and freshen up. Then come back.'

She tried to think about it, but she was too tired. She closed her eyes and tried to think about it again. After a time, she said, 'Maybe I will go home for a few minutes. Maybe if I'm not just sitting right here watching him every second, he'll wake up and be all right. You know? Maybe he'll wake up if I'm not here. I'll go home and take a bath and put on clean clothes. I'll feed Slug. Then I'll come back.'

'I'll be right here,' he said. 'You go on home, honey. I'll keep an eye on things here.' His eyes were bloodshot and small, as if he'd been drinking for a long time. His clothes were rumpled. His beard had come out again. She touched his face, and then she took her hand back. She understood he wanted to be by himself for a while, not have to talk or share his worry for a time. She picked her purse up from the nightstand, and he helped her into her coat.

'I won't be gone long,' she said.

'Just sit and rest for a little while when you get home,' he said. 'Eat something. Take a bath. After you get out of the bath, just sit for a while and rest. It'll do you a world of good, you'll see. Then come back,' he said. 'Let's try not to worry. You heard what Dr Francis said.'

She stood in her coat for a minute trying to recall the doctor's exact words, looking for any nuances, any hint of something behind his words other than what he had said. She tried to remember if his expression had changed any when he bent over to examine the child. She remembered the way his features had composed themselves as he rolled back the child's eyelids and then listened to his breathing.

She went to the door, where she turned and looked back. She looked at the child, and then she looked at the father. Howard nodded. She stepped out of the room and pulled the door closed behind her.

She went past the nurses' station and down to the end of the corridor, looking for the elevator. At the end of the corridor, she turned to her right and entered a little waiting room where a Negro family sat in wicker chairs. There was a middle-aged man in a khaki shirt and pants, a baseball cap pushed back on his head. A large woman wearing a housedress and slippers was slumped in one of the chairs. A teenaged girl in jeans, hair done in dozens of little braids, lay stretched out in one of the chairs smoking a cigarette, her legs crossed at the ankles. The family swung their eyes to Ann as she entered the room. The little table was littered with hamburger wrappers and Styrofoam cups.

'Franklin,' the large woman said as she roused herself. 'Is it about Franklin?' Her eyes widened. 'Tell me now, lady,' the woman said. 'Is it about Franklin?' She was trying to rise from her chair, but the man had closed his hand over her arm.

'Here, here,' he said. 'Evelyn.'

'I'm sorry,' Ann said. 'I'm looking for the elevator. My son is in the hospital, and now I can't find the elevator.'

'Elevator is down that way, turn left,' the man said as he aimed a finger.

The girl drew on her cigarette and stared at Ann. Her eyes were narrowed to slits, and her broad lips parted slowly as she let the smoke escape. The Negro woman let her head fall on her shoulder and looked away from Ann, no longer interested.

'My son was hit by a car,' Ann said to the man. She seemed to need to explain herself. 'He has a concussion and a little skull fracture, but he's going to be all right. He's in shock now, but it might be some kind of coma, too. That's what really worries us, the coma part. I'm going out for a little while, but my husband is with him. Maybe he'll wake up while I'm gone.'

'That's too bad,' the man said and shifted in the chair. He shook his head. He looked down at the table, and then he looked back at Ann. She was still standing there. He said, 'Our Franklin, he's on the operating table. Somebody cut him. Tried to kill him. There was a fight where he was at. At this party. They say he was just standing and watching. Not bothering nobody. But that don't mean nothing these days. Now he's on the operating table. We're just hoping and praying, that's all we can do now.' He gazed at her steadily.

Ann looked at the girl again, who was still watching her, and at the older woman, who kept her head down, but whose eyes were now closed. Ann saw the lips moving silently, making words. She had an urge to ask what those words were. She wanted to talk more with these people who were in the same kind of waiting she was in. She was afraid, and they were afraid. They had that in common. She would have liked to have said something else about the accident, told them more about Scotty, that it had happened on the day of his birthday, Monday, and that he was still unconscious. Yet she didn't know how to begin. She stood looking at them without saying anything more.

She went down the corridor the man had indicated and found the elevator. She waited a minute in front of the closed doors, still wondering if she was doing the right thing. Then she put out her finger and touched the button.

She pulled into the driveway and cut the engine. She closed her eyes and leaned her head against the wheel for a minute. She listened to the ticking sounds the engine made as it began to cool. Then she got out of the car. She could hear the dog barking inside the house. She went to the front door, which was unlocked. She went inside and turned on lights and put on a kettle of water for tea. She opened some dogfood and fed Slug on the back porch. The dog ate in hungry little smacks. It kept running into the kitchen to see that she was going to stay. As she sat down on the sofa with her tea, the telephone rang.

'Yes!' she said as she answered. 'Hello!'

'Mrs Weiss,' a man's voice said. It was five o'clock in the morning, and she thought she could hear machinery or equipment of some kind in the background.

'Yes, yes! What is it?' she said. 'This is Mrs Weiss. This is she. What is it, please?' She listened to whatever it was in the background. 'Is it Scotty, for Christ's sake?'

'Scotty,' the man's voice said. 'It's about Scotty, yes. It has to do with Scotty, that problem. Have you forgotten about Scotty?' the man said. Then he hung up.

She dialed the hospital's number and asked for the third floor. She demanded information about her son from the nurse who answered the telephone. Then she asked to speak to her husband. It was, she said, an emergency.

She waited, turning the telephone cord in her fingers. She closed her eyes and felt sick at her stomach. She would have to make herself eat. Slug came in from the back porch and lay down near her feet. He wagged his tail. She pulled at his ear while he licked her fingers. Howard was on the line.

'Somebody just called here,' she said. She twisted the telephone cord. 'He said it was about Scotty,' she cried.

'Scotty's fine,' Howard told her. 'I mean, he's still sleeping. There's been no change. The nurse has been in twice since you've been gone. A nurse or else a doctor. He's all right.'

'This man called. He said it was about Scotty,' she told him.

'Honey, you rest for a little while, you need the rest. It must be that same caller I had. Just forget it. Come back down here after you've rested. Then we'll have breakfast or something.'

'Breakfast,' she said. 'I don't want any breakfast.'

'You know what I mean,' he said. 'Juice, something. I don't know. I don't know anything, Ann. Jesus, I'm not hungry, either. Ann, it's hard to talk now. I'm standing here at the desk. Dr Francis is coming again at eight o'clock this morning. He's going to have something to tell us then, something more definite. That's what one of the nurses said. She didn't know any more than that. Ann? Honey, maybe we'll know something more then. At eight o'clock. Come back here before eight. Meanwhile, I'm right here and Scotty's all right. He's still the same,' he added.

'I was drinking a cup of tea,' she said, 'when the telephone rang. They said it was about Scotty. There was a noise in the background. Was there a noise in the background on that call you had, Howard?'

'I don't remember,' he said. 'Maybe the driver of the car, maybe he's a psychopath and found out about Scotty somehow. But I'm here with him. Just rest like you were going to do. Take a bath and come back by seven or so, and we'll talk to the doctor together when he gets here. It's going to be all right, honey. I'm here, and there are doctors and nurses around. They say his condition is stable.'

'I'm scared to death,' she said.

She ran water, undressed, and got into the tub. She washed and dried quickly, not taking the time to wash her hair. She put on clean underwear, wool slacks, and a sweater. She went into the living room, where the dog looked up at her and let its tail thump once against the floor. It was just starting to get light outside when she went out to the car.

She drove into the parking lot of the hospital and found a space close to the front door. She felt she was in some obscure way responsible for what had happened to the child. She let her thoughts move to the Negro family. She remembered the name Franklin and the table that was covered with hamburger papers, and the teenaged girl staring at her as she drew on her cigarette. 'Don't have children,' she told the girl's image as she entered the front door of the hospital. 'For God's sake, don't.'

She took the elevator up to the third floor with two nurses who were just going on duty. It was Wednesday morning, a few minutes before seven. There was a page for a Dr Madison as the elevator doors slid open on the third floor. She got off behind the nurses, who turned in the other direction and continued the conversation she had interrupted when she'd gotten into the elevator. She walked down the corridor to the little alcove where the Negro family had been waiting. They were gone now, but the chairs were scattered in such a way that it looked as if people had just jumped up from them the minute before. The tabletop was cluttered with the same cups and papers, the ashtray was filled with cigarette butts.

She stopped at the nurses' station. A nurse was standing behind the counter, brushing her hair and yawning.

'There was a Negro boy in surgery last night,' Ann said. 'Franklin was his name. His family was in the waiting room, I'd like to inquire about his condition.'

A nurse who was sitting at a desk behind the counter looked up from a chart in front of her. The telephone buzzed and she picked up the receiver, but she kept her eyes on Ann.

'He passed away,' said the nurse at the counter. The nurse held the hairbrush and kept looking at her. 'Are you a friend of the family or what?'

'I met the family last night,' Ann said. 'My own son is in the hospital. I guess he's in shock. We don't know for sure what's wrong. I just wondered about Franklin, that's all. Thank you.' She moved down the corridor. Elevator doors the same color as the walls slid open and a gaunt, bald man in white pants and white canvas shoes pulled a heavy cart off the elevator. She hadn't noticed these doors last night. The man wheeled the cart out into the corridor and stopped in front of the room nearest the elevator and consulted a clipboard. Then he reached down and slid a tray out of the cart. He rapped lightly on the door and entered the room. She could smell the unpleasant odors of warm food as she passed the cart. She hurried on without looking at any of the nurses and pushed open the door to the child's room.

Howard was standing at the window with his hands behind his back. He turned around as she came in.

'How is he?' she said. She went over to the bed. She dropped her purse on the floor beside the nightstand. It seemed to her she had been gone a long time. She touched the child's face. 'Howard?'

'Dr Francis was here a little while ago,' Howard said. She looked at him closely and thought his shoulders were bunched a little.

'I thought he wasn't coming until eight o'clock this morning,' she said quickly.

'There was another doctor with him. A neurologist.'

'A neurologist,' she said.

Howard nodded. His shoulders were bunching, she could see that. 'What'd they say, Howard? For Christ's sake, what'd they say? What is it?'

'They said they're going to take him down and run more tests on him, Ann. They think they're going to operate, honey. Honey, they *are* going to operate. They can't figure out why he won't wake up. It's more than just shock or concussion, they know that much now. It's in his skull, the fracture, it has something, something to do with that, they think. So they're going to operate. I tried to call you, but I guess you'd already left the house.'

'Oh, God,' she said. 'Oh, please, Howard, please,' she said, taking his arms.

'Look!' Howard said, 'Scotty! Look, Ann!' He turned her toward the bed.

The boy had opened his eyes, then closed them. He opened them again now. The eyes stared straight ahead for a minute, then moved slowly in his head until they rested on Howard and Ann, then traveled away again.

'Scotty,' his mother said, moving to the bed.

'Hey, Scott,' his father said. 'Hey, son.'

They leaned over the bed. Howard took the child's hand in his hands and began to pat and squeeze the hand. Ann bent over the boy and kissed his forehead again and again. She put her hands over either side of his face. 'Scotty, honey, it's Mummy and Daddy,' she said. 'Scotty?'

The boy looked at them, but without any sign of recognition. Then his mouth opened, his eyes scrunched closed, and he howled until he had no more air in his lungs. His face seemed to relax and soften then. His lips parted as his last breath was puffed through his throat and exhaled gently through the clenched teeth.

The doctors called it a hidden occlusion and said it was a one-in-a-million circumstance. Maybe if it could have been detected somehow and surgery undertaken immediately, they could have saved him. But more than likely not. In any case, what would they have been looking for? Nothing had shown up in the tests or in the X-rays.

Dr Francis was shaken. 'I can't tell you how badly I feel. I'm so very sorry, I can't tell you,' he said as he led them into the doctors' lounge. There was a doctor sitting in a chair with his legs hooked over the back of another chair, watching an early-morning TV show. He was wearing a green delivery-room outfit, loose green pants and green blouse, and a green cap that covered his hair. He looked at Howard and Ann and then looked at Dr Francis. He got to his feet and turned off the set and went out of the room. Dr Francis guided Ann to the sofa, sat down beside her, and began to talk in a low, consoling voice. At one point, he leaned over and embraced her. She could feel his chest rising and falling evenly against her shoulder. She kept her eyes open and let him hold her. Howard went into the bathroom, but he left the door open.

After a violent fit of weeping, he ran water and washed his face. Then he came out and sat down at the little table that held a telephone. He looked at the telephone as though deciding what to do first. He made some calls. After a time, Dr Francis used the telephone.

'Is there anything else I can do for the moment?' he asked them.

Howard shook his head. Ann stared at Dr Francis as if unable to comprehend his words.

The doctor walked them to the hospital's front door. People were entering and leaving the hospital. It was eleven o'clock in the morning. Ann was aware of how slowly, almost reluctantly, she moved her feet. It seemed to her that Dr Francis was making them leave when she felt they should stay, when it would be more the right thing to do to stay. She gazed out into the parking lot and then turned around and looked back at the front of the hospital. She began shaking her head. 'No, no,' she said. 'I can't leave him here, no.' She heard herself say that and thought how unfair it was that the only words that came out were the sort of words used on TV shows where people were stunned by violent or sudden deaths. She wanted her words to be her own. 'No,' she said, and for some reason the memory of the Negro woman's head lolling on the woman's shoulder came to her. 'No,' she said again.

'I'll be talking to you later in the day,' the doctor was saying to Howard. 'There are still some things that have to be done, things that have to be cleared up to our satisfaction. Some things that need explaining.'

'An autopsy,' Howard said.

Dr Francis nodded.

'I understand,' Howard said. Then he said, 'Oh, Jesus. No, I don't understand, doctor. I can't, I can't. I just can't.'

Dr Francis put his arm around Howard's shoulders. 'I'm sorry. God, how I'm sorry.' He let go of Howard's shoulders and held out his hand. Howard looked at the hand, and then he took it. Dr Francis put his arms around Ann once more. He seemed full of some goodness she didn't understand. She let her head rest on his shoulder, but her eyes stayed open. She kept looking at the hospital. As they drove out of the parking lot, she looked back at the hospital.

*   *   *

At home, she sat on the sofa with her hands in her coat pockets. Howard closed the door to the child's room. He got the coffee-maker going and then he found an empty box. He had thought to pick up some of the child's things that were scattered around the living room. But instead he sat down beside her on the sofa, pushed the box to one side, and leaned forward, arms between his knees. He began to weep. She pulled his head over into her lap and patted his shoulder. 'He's gone,' she said. She kept patting his shoulder. Over his sobs, she could hear the coffee-maker hissing in the kitchen. 'There, there,' she said tenderly. 'Howard, he's gone. He's gone and now we'll have to get used to that. To being alone.'

In a little while, Howard got up and began moving aimlessly around the room with the box, not putting anything into it, but collecting some things together on the floor at one end of the sofa. She continued to sit with her hands in her coat pockets. Howard put the box down and brought coffee into the living room. Later, Ann made calls to relatives. After each call had been placed and the party had answered, Ann would blurt out a few words and cry for a minute. Then she would quietly explain, in a measured voice, what had happened, and tell them about arrangements. Howard took the box out to the garage, where he saw the child's bicycle. He dropped the box and sat down on the pavement beside the bicycle. He took hold of the bicycle awkwardly so that it leaned against his chest. He held it, the rubber pedal sticking into his chest. He gave the wheel a turn.

Ann hung up the telephone after talking to her sister. She was looking up another number when the telephone rang. She picked up on the first ring.

'Hello,' she said, and she heard something in the background, a humming noise. 'Hello!' she said. 'For God's sake,' she said. 'Who is this? What is it you want?'

'Your Scotty, I got him ready for you,' the man's voice said. 'Did you forget him?'

'You evil bastard!' she shouted into the receiver. 'How can you do this, you evil son of a bitch?'

'Scotty,' the man said. 'Have you forgotten about Scotty?' Then the man hung up on her.

Howard heard the shouting and came in to find her with her head on her arms over the table, weeping. He picked up the receiver and listened to the dial tone.

Much later, just before midnight, after they had dealt with many things, the telephone rang again.

'You answer it,' she said. 'Howard, it's him, I know.' They were sitting at the kitchen table with coffee in front of them. Howard had a small glass of whiskey beside his cup. He answered on the third ring.

'Hello,' he said. 'Who is this? Hello! Hello!' The line went dead. 'He hung up,' Howard said. 'Whoever it was.'

'It was him,' she said. 'That bastard. I'd like to kill him,' she said. 'I'd like to shoot him and watch him kick,' she said.

'Ann, my God,' he said.

'Could you hear anything?' she said. 'In the background? A noise, machinery, something humming?'

'Nothing, really. Nothing like that,' he said. 'There wasn't much time. I think there was some radio music. Yes, there was a radio going, that's all I could tell. I don't know what in God's name is going on,' he said.

She shook her head. 'If I could, could get my hands on him.' It came to her then. She knew who it was. Scotty, the cake, the telephone number. She pushed the chair away from the table and got up. 'Drive me down to the shopping center,' she said. 'Howard.'

'What are you saying?'

'The shopping center. I know who it is who's calling. I know who it is. It's the baker, the son-of-a-bitching baker, Howard. I had him bake a cake for Scotty's birthday. That's who's calling. That's who has the number and keeps calling us. To harass us about that cake. The baker, that bastard.'

They drove down to the shopping center. The sky was clear and stars were out. It was cold, and they ran the heater in the car. They parked in front of the bakery. All of the shops and stores were closed, but there were cars at the far end of the lot in front of the movie theater. The bakery windows were dark, but when they looked through the glass they could see a light in the back room and, now and then, a big man in an apron moving in and out of the white, even light. Through the glass, she could see the display cases and some little tables with chairs. She tried the door. She rapped on the glass. But if the baker heard them, he gave no sign. He didn't look in their direction.

They drove around behind the bakery and parked. They got out of the car. There was a lighted window too high up for them to see inside. A sign near the back door said THE PANTRY BAKERY, SPECIAL ORDERS. She could hear faintly a radio playing inside and something creak – an oven door as it was pulled down? She knocked on the door and waited. Then she knocked again, louder. The radio was turned down and there was a scraping sound now, the distinct sound of something, a drawer, being pulled open and then closed.

Someone unlocked the door and opened it. The baker stood in the light and peered out at them. 'I'm closed for business,' he said. 'What do you want at this hour? It's midnight. Are you drunk or something?'

She stepped into the light that fell through the open door. He blinked his heavy eyelids as he recognized her. 'It's you,' he said.

'It's me,' she said. 'Scotty's mother. This is Scotty's father. We'd like to come in.'

The baker said, 'I'm busy now. I have work to do.'

She had stepped inside the doorway anyway. Howard came in behind her. The baker moved back. 'It smells like a bakery in here. Doesn't it smell like a bakery in here, Howard?'

'What do you want?' the baker said. 'Maybe you want your cake? That's it, you decided you want your cake. You ordered a cake, didn't you?'

'You're pretty smart for a baker,' she said. 'Howard, this is the man who's been calling us.' She clenched her fists. She stared at him fiercely. There was a deep burning inside her, an anger that made her feel larger than herself, larger than either of these men.

'Just a minute here,' the baker said. 'You want to pick up your three-day-old cake? That it? I don't want to argue with you, lady. There it sits over there, getting stale. I'll give it to you for half of what I quoted you. No. You want it? You can have it. It's no good to me, no good to anyone now. It cost me time and money to make that cake. If you want it, okay, if you don't, that's okay, too. I have to get back to work.' He looked at them and rolled his tongue behind his teeth.

'More cakes,' she said. She knew she was in control of it, of what was increasing in her. She was calm.

'Lady, I work sixteen hours a day in this place to earn a living,' the baker said. He wiped his hands on his apron. 'I work night and day in here, trying to make ends meet.' A look crossed Ann's face that made the baker move back and say, 'No trouble, now.' He reached to the counter and picked up a rolling pin with his right hand and began to tap it against the palm of his other hand. 'You want the cake or not? I have to get back to work. Bakers work at night,' he said again. His eyes were small, mean-looking, she thought, nearly lost in the bristly flesh around his cheeks. His neck was thick with fat.

'I know bakers work at night,' Ann said. 'They make phone calls at night, too. You bastard,' she said.

The baker continued to tap the rolling pin against his hand. He glanced at Howard. 'Careful, careful,' he said to Howard.

'My son's dead,' she said with a cold, even finality. 'He was hit by a car Monday morning. We've been waiting with him, until he died. But, of course, you couldn't be expected to know that, could you? Bakers can't know everything – can they, Mr Baker? But he's dead. He's dead, you bastard!' Just as suddenly as it had welled in her, the anger dwindled, gave way to something else, a dizzy feeling of nausea. She leaned against the wooden table that was sprinkled with flour, put her hands over her face, and began to cry, her shoulders rocking back and forth. 'It isn't fair,' she said. 'It isn't, isn't fair. '

Howard put his hand at the small of her back and looked at the baker. 'Shame on you,' Howard said to him. 'Shame.'

The baker put the rolling pin back on the counter. He undid his apron and threw it on the counter. He pulled a chair out from under the card table that held papers and receipts, an adding machine, and a telephone directory. 'Please sit down,' he said. 'Let me get you a chair,' he said to Howard. 'Sit down now, please.' The baker went into the front of the shop and returned with two little wrought-iron chairs. 'Please sit down, you people.'

Ann wiped her eyes and looked at the baker. 'I wanted to kill you,' she said. 'I wanted you dead.'

The baker had cleared a space for them at the table. He shoved the adding machine to one side, along with the stacks of notepaper and receipts. He pushed the telephone directory onto the floor, where it landed with a thud. Howard and Ann sat down and pulled their chairs up to the table. The baker sat down, too.

'Let me say how sorry I am,' the baker said, putting his elbows on the table. 'God alone knows how sorry. Listen to me. I'm just a baker. I don't claim to be anything else. Maybe once, maybe years ago, I was a different kind of human being. I've forgotten, I don't know for sure. But I'm not any longer, if I ever was. Now I'm just a baker. That don't excuse my doing what I did, I know. But I'm deeply sorry. I'm sorry for your son, and sorry for my part in this,' the baker said. He spread his hands out on the table and turned them over to reveal his palms. 'I don't have any children myself, so I can only imagine what you must be feeling. All I can say to you now is that I'm sorry. Forgive me, if you can,' the baker said. 'I'm not an evil man, I don't think. Not evil, like you said on the phone. You got to understand what it comes down to is I don't know how to act anymore, it would seem. Please,' the man said, 'let me ask you if you can find it in your hearts to forgive me?'

It was warm inside the bakery. Howard stood up from the table and took off his coat. He helped Ann from her coat. The baker looked at them for a minute and then nodded and got up from the table. He went to the oven and turned off some switches. He found cups and poured coffee from an electric coffee-maker. He put a carton of cream on the table, and a bowl of sugar.

'You probably need to eat something,' the baker said. 'I hope you'll eat some of my hot rolls. You have to eat and keep going. Eating is a small, good thing in a time like this,' he said.

He served them warm cinnamon rolls just out of the oven, the icing still runny. He put butter on the table and knives to spread the butter. Then the baker sat down at the table with them. He waited. He waited until they each took a roll from the platter and began to eat. 'It's good to eat something,' he said, watching them. 'There's more. Eat up. Eat all you want. There's all the rolls in the world in here.'

They ate rolls and drank coffee. Ann was suddenly hungry, and the rolls were warm and sweet. She ate three of them, which pleased the baker. Then he began to talk. They listened carefully. Although they were tired and in anguish, they listened to what the baker had to say. They nodded when the baker began to speak of loneliness, and of the sense of doubt and limitation that had come to him in his middle years. He told them what it was like to be childless all these years. To repeat the days with the ovens endlessly full and endlessly empty. The party food, the celebrations he'd worked over. Icing knuckle-deep. The tiny wedding couples stuck into cakes. Hundreds of them, no, thousands by now. Birthdays. Just imagine all those candles burning. He had a necessary trade. He was a baker. He was glad he wasn't a florist. It was better to be feeding people. This was a better smell anytime than flowers.

'Smell this,' the baker said, breaking open a dark loaf. 'It's a heavy bread, but rich.' They smelled it, then he had them taste it. It had the taste of molasses and coarse grains. They listened to him. They ate what they could. They swallowed the dark bread. It was like daylight under the fluorescent trays of light. They talked on into the early morning, the high, pale cast of light in the windows, and they did not think of leaving.

Raymond Carver

Working on A Small Good Thing

1. The opening of the story
● Read the opening four paragraphs of this story and then stop where it says, 'She thanked him and drove home.'
● What do you notice about the style of writing and the way the writer presents the elements of the story? You might like to think about some of the following:

– how much detail is included
– whether the story seems to move quickly or slowly
– how the characters are introduced and to what effect
– whether the writer seems to want to involve you in the story and with the characters or not
– whether the writing style is detached or involved (give some examples)

2. Before reading the rest of the story
The quotes re-printed below are taken from the rest of the story.
● Read them out and discuss your ideas about the rest of the story, bearing in mind what you already know about it from the beginning. You might talk about:

– the plot
– the characters
– the kind of story it is going to be (start by talking about whether it reminds you of stories you have read or seen or written already)
– the themes or ideas it might be exploring

At some point in your discussion, try making a list of questions that these quotes leave you asking about the rest of the story.

> 'Of course, the birthday party was canceled ...'

> 'a bit of concussion ...'

> 'this creep who keeps calling ...'

'I've been praying ...'

'Somebody cut him ...'

'She wanted to talk more with these people who were in the same kind of waiting she was in ...'

'Don't have children ...'

'he howled until he had no more air in his lungs ...'

'I don't know how to act any more ...'

'warm cinnamon rolls just out of the oven, the icing still runny ...'

——————————————————————— *After reading* ———

3. The parents and the baker
● Re-read the ending from page 44 where it says, 'They drove down to the shopping center ...' to the end.
● The quotes re-printed on the next page have been taken from this final section. Read them out and talk about them in pairs. Think about the following:

– what associations and ideas do these words and phrases hold for you?
– which three quotes do you think are particularly important and why?
– what impression of the parents and the baker is the writer leaving you with?

'a big man in an apron moving in and out of the white, even light ...'

'He's dead you bastard!'

'She leaned against the wooden table that was sprinkled with flour, put her hands over her face, and began to cry ...'

'He spread his hands out on the table and turned them over to reveal his palms ...'

'I don't know how to act any more it would seem...'

'It was warm inside the bakery ...'

'"Eating is a small good thing in a time like this" he said ...'

'the rolls were warm and sweet ...'

'the baker began to speak of loneliness ...'

'They swallowed the dark bread ...'

'they did not think of leaving ...'

● Talk about what the ending is like and what effect it has on you as a reader.

4. Two endings

Raymond Carver experimented with a different version of this story, calling it 'The Bath'. This story is shorter and ends with the mother leaving her son, who is still alive but in a coma, and going home to take a bath. Here is how 'The Bath' ends:

> 'She pulled into the driveway. The dog ran out from behind the house. He
> ran in circles on the grass. She closed her eyes and leaned her head against
> the wheel. She listened to the ticking of the engine.
>
> She got out of the car and went to the door. She turned on lights and put on
> water for tea. She opened a can and fed the dog. She sat down on the sofa with
> her tea.
>
> The telephone rang.
>
> 'Yes!' she said. 'Hello!' she said.
>
> 'Mrs Weiss,' a man's voice said.
>
> 'Yes,' she said. 'This is Mrs Weiss. Is it about Scotty?' she said.
>
> 'Scotty,' the voice said. 'It is about Scotty,' the voice said. 'It has to do with
> Scotty, yes.' '

● Talk about this alternative ending and what effect it has on you as a reader. How
does it compare with the ending of 'A Small Good Thing'? Which do you prefer and
why?

5. The scenes with the black family
● Re-read the scenes at the nurses' station on pages 38 and 41 where Ann talks to
the black family in the waiting room, and then later when she finds out their son has
died. What are your reactions to these scenes? Why do you think Raymond Carver
has included them?

6. Exploring the story from different viewpoints
This story pays very close attention to the main people in it – the mother and the
father.
● Write a short piece from the point of view of one of the other characters in the
story. You could try one of the following situations:

– Dr Francis at home the night after the boy has died
– some time later, the baker tells a friend about the night Ann and Howard came to
his bakery

7. The writing style
A reviewer in *Newsweek*, an American magazine, said that Raymond Carver's 'laconic,
unadorned style equips him perfectly to conjure up marginal lives of quiet
desperation.'
● Using a dictionary if you need to, look at each of the key elements of this
statement in turn to work out what they mean.
● Decide whether you agree that he is writing about 'marginal lives of quiet
desperation'.
● Look through the story for examples of a deliberately plain and condensed writing
style. Write them down and discuss their effect on you and their purpose in the story
as a whole. It might help your discussion of style to try rewriting some of your
examples in the opposite style, as very dramatic, emotional and overdone.

8. A film treatment

● Working with a partner, try turning this story into a treatment for a film. A treatment involves summarising the story, descibing its locations, characters and visual style, and suggesting the way it should be filmed, cast and directed. In your planning, talk about the following things:

– How would you organise the narrative? Should it be chronological or told in 'flashbacks'?
– Should the story be told continuously, or would you break it up with sub-plots or contrasting storylines? What would be the effect of each of these different options on the emotional impact of the story?
– Who should become the central character or 'voice' of the story?
– How would you dramatise the thoughts and feelings of the different characters?
– Would you need to create any new characters or plot developments to sustain the tension in the story?
– Who ideally would you cast to play the mother, father and baker?
– How would you end the story?

● When you have prepared your treatment, compare it with others in your group. In your own time you could watch the version of the story in the film *Short Cuts*, which is based on a selection of Carver's stories and is directed by Robert Altman.

9. Comparative work – the death of a child

'A Small Good Thing' and 'The Schoolteacher's Guest' explore parental grief at the loss of a child, but their focus and style are very different.
● Use these headings to help you chart similarities and differences between the two stories:

– what aspects of the death of the child the writer focuses on
– whose eyes we see it through
– how it is narrated
– what kind of tone it is written in
– whether it is realistic or fantastic in its style

10. Comparative work – third person narratives

Several stories in this anthology are written as third person narratives. 'A Small Good Thing', 'Joebell and America', 'White Places' and 'Mrs Turner Cutting the Grass' all have very different third person narrators and quite different styles of narration.
● Choose two or three of these stories that contrast with each other and write about how differently the writers use this way of telling their story. You might want to use some of these ideas to help you:

– what language does the narrator use?
– how detached/ involved is the narration?
– does the narrator use irony, direct addresses to the reader, indications of his/her own viewpoint to make a relationship with the reader?
– what is the tone of the narration?

11. Comparative work – death

Look at the suggestions for comparative work after the story, 'Spirit'.

12. Wider reading

● 'The Bath' by Raymond Carver is a shorter version of 'A Small Good Thing'. Raymond Carver's short stories can be found in a collection called *Short Cuts*. There is a film version of these stories, directed by Robert Altman.

● Carver's collections of poems *In A Marine Light* and *New Path to the Waterfall* have a similar condensed clarity to his short stories.

● *The Sweet Hereafter* by Russell Banks is a novel about a school bus crash in a small American town. The writer uses the event to reveal the complex emotional lives of the ordinary families involved.

White Places

Celeste was first cousin to Cissy and Killer. Peachey was Celeste's Best, meaning her best friend. They always said 'Bests' to keep their true relationship a secret, and to be able to talk about the secret without hurting anyone else's feelings. That was the important thing, Celeste said, that no one know and that no one get their feelings hurt. Of course Cissy and Killer knew, but that was all right because they were first cousins to Celeste and so practically first cousins to Peachey.

The four of them had a club. The name and nature of this club was changed every three or four weeks, depending on what Celeste was reading. Celeste talked like a book and was fond of titles. She liked being President, Secretary, Madam Chairman and Grand Duchess. Genevra Samantha Roberta della Rocca of Upper Vernocopium, a place even more important than Oz. The others let her be. But everyone knew it was Cissy who ruled.

Killer was the youngest and the fattest. Her shoes were always wet and untied with her socks sliding down into the heels. She had cold sores and was only in fourth grade. Her name was not really Killer. It was Charlotte Mundy Fletcher Doyle (mixed marriage: Roman Catholic and Presbyterian). Like just about every awful thing, the nickname was an invention of Cissy's. It came from one of their earliest games in which she and Celeste, starlets sharing an apartment in Beverly Hills, were stalked by a dangerous maniac known simply as The Killer. Their pretend boyfriends, a producer and his brother, the world's most daring stunt man, came over and over again to their rescue. Over and over they carried off Killer, bound and gagged, to a lunatic asylum. That was how it began – a crude game by later standards, but the name stuck. Cissy's and Celeste's parents tried, without success, to stop the children calling her by it.

'Chaaaaarrrrrrlotte,' Cissy would sneer across the dinner table, 'pass the potatoes, Chaaaarrrrlotte.' Cissy wasn't afraid of anything. Eventually though, when she behaved like this, she would be sent off to bed where she would lie awake, waiting to pinch her sister's fingers with the nutcracker as soon as she fell asleep, which was usually within three minutes.

Mrs Doyle insisted the others be nice to Killer, share with her. Once she even had cried when her youngest daughter came home wet, though uncomplaining, from the swamp. They had been on a Royal Expedition up the Nile, led by Robert Redford and Cissy in a sedan chair. Killer had been thrown to the crocodiles after attempting to kidnap the baby Moses. Later, Killer had listened with her ear to the door as her mother reprimanded Cissy.

'Cissy, why are you so mean to Killer –' She stopped impatiently. 'Oh for heaven's sake, you know I mean *Charlotte*. It was too late. Mummy had said it and that made it true for ever.

Killer was six then, and Cissy was eight. By now the Pretends were much more complicated, and included a wide range of malice and glamour. (Cissy was maddeningly inventive.) But they were still variants on a single theme, and always ended with the Finding Out, the unmasking, at which everyone ran shrieking from Killer. Why the others liked pretending to be weak and frightened and in danger when really they were so strong, stronger than she would ever be, Killer could not understand.

A tried and true Pretend, used when all else had ended in boredom or hair-pulling, was The Crazy Doctor. Killer, in disguise, would come to the grown-ups' bedroom – it had to begin in there – to prescribe for one of the three, who were always orphaned sisters. Eventually, they would guess her wicked intentions and race, screaming and laughing, to the attic, down again, through the upstairs rooms and out on to the lawn, pursued by Killer who was well-versed in the terrifying snorts and snarls she was required to make. Once outside, she would be caught, rolled up in a blanket, tied and taken off to be burnt at the stake, then released and made to play her part all over again until parents put a stop to the game.

They spent school vacations at each other's houses. Easter at the Doyles' and Christmas at Celeste's. This time, Peachey would be with them. Peachey was too small for her age, but very energetic. She was called Peachey because she once had been taught by her father to respond, at the top of her chipmunk voice to all enquiries after her condition with the answer 'Peachey Keeno!'

Celeste's father and mother were very indulgent. Even when the girls kept them awake until four in the morning, they did not complain very much. Killer always fell asleep first. The others ate crackers in bed and pushed the crumbs on to her side. They made raids to the kitchen for peanut butter sandwiches at 2.00 a.m. They came back and covered Killer's face with toothpaste. By the beam of a flashlight, they held a club meeting and read comic books under the covers. Peachey wrapped all their apple cores in paper and put the bundle down the toilet. The next morning the plumbing was blocked, and Killer stood, serious-eyed (she had been banished by the girls until three), watching Aunty Lillian mop up the bathroom on her hands and knees. She was given a jelly doughnut and allowed to watch *Tom and Jerry* until called to come and be a werewolf.

There was a blizzard. Killer was frightened by the silence and by the way the snow climbed the window panes. When she pressed her face against them, she imagined that she had gone blind, but that her blindness was white instead of black. It seemed hard to breathe, and she wondered if everyone were going to be buried alive. She thought she might like to go home. It would be nice to be tucked in by her mother and to watch her baby brother kicking his feet like a small fat bug or dribbling breakfast down his pyjamas. But she was too scared to tell Aunty Lillian any of these things. Besides, she had to stay here and be a Body Snatcher.

Celeste said that they should make puppets and a theatre and put on a puppet show. They thought of nothing else for the three days the blizzard lasted. Cissy and Celeste wrote a play and made posters to advertise the event, while Peachey and Killer worked happily and messily with balloons, cardboard tubes and papier mâché. Aunt Lillian was very patient. She and Uncle Raymond, along with all of Celeste's and Peachey's dolls, were forced to attend three performances, and to applaud, exclaim and congratulate on each occasion.

They experimented with the left-over flour and water paste, and invented, by the addition of sugar, milk, vanilla, corn syrup and a dash of laundry starch, a drink which they called Plush and which they forced Killer to taste after the addition of each new ingredient. That evening Killer threw up her supper. Cissy said that she thought it was disgusting, and that Killer was not mature enough to have been allowed to come.

When the storm ended, they put up signs and tried to sell Plush from a snow fort which they built at the end of the driveway. The snow was very high there, nearly six feet, because the blizzard had been such a long one and the snow-plough had had to come around so many times. No one bought the drink but Uncle Raymond who tasted it, tried to smile, and said he would finish the rest in the house, if that was all right with 'you girls'. They lost interest in Plush. It turned sour, stank and Aunty Lillian carefully asked permission to throw it out.

They decided to enlarge the snow fort. They built half a dozen each winter and knew everything about their construction. This was to be the biggest they had ever made. To celebrate its completion, Cissy said, they must make up a brand new Pretend. Celeste agreed. Then Peachey and Killer agreed. They worked even harder on the snow fort than they had on the puppet show, talking and planning every minute for the Important Celebration Pretend. They were very excited, Killer could tell. She saw how much it thrilled them to make believe. To her, inside, it seemed almost frightening, the way they were always at it, never never getting tired of it. Why did they want to be something they weren't, to change everything into what it wasn't? Killer liked everything as it was – just plain with no Pretend, no titles, no talking like books, no ruling, no dressing up, no punishments, no Madam Chairman or Grand Duchesses or Cleopatras. But that was her secret. She knew that somehow it was wrong to like everything as it was, just plain. So she didn't dare tell them what she really liked.

What she liked was what they were doing now: sitting on top of their snow fort, watching people go by on the street – slipping and sliding, it was so funny – smelling the snow and sucking silently on the long icicles that hung from the maple trees and that tasted so sweet. Killer sat and sucked and felt happy to be with the others, happy about not having to do fractions, happy about the graham crackers and marshmallow they would be eating at four when Pretend was over.

Peachey, in a burst of Peachey energy, put snow down the back of her neck. Killer was soaked through anyway. They all were. But they hardly noticed, they were so warm with activity.

'Now this is the game,' Cissy announced, 'and you have to remember it. We've decided, so no changing the rules. Me and Celeste and Peachey are sisters and we're of noble birth. Our *real* mother dies and our father the Duke marries this woman Elvira, who pretends to be nice but who isn't – who's evil really. That's you Killer. You have to *seem* nice at first, remember that, otherwise you'll spoil everything. Then we find out that Elvira has killed our *real* mother and is plotting to kill our father and steal our inheritance and make us homeless orphans. Then – this is Celeste's part, she invented it, she says I have to say so – a prince saves us! He catches Elvira making a cowardly escape. Then he marries Celeste and introduces me and Peachey to his two brothers who are Paul Newman and Steve McQueen. Elvira goes to prison. Do you hear that, Killer? Are you listening? You're going to be shut up in the snow fort – don't interrupt me, you *have* to be. Do you want to spoil the game for everyone else? That *would* be something you'd do. Anyway, my word is law, so you're going to prison. We'll come back for you after we've been to the palace to recover our gold and attend the banquet.'

'But – what about my graham crackers?' Killer knew she mustn't cry.

'You can have them later – if you do everything you're supposed to.'

'OK.'

Now they were carrying out the dolls to be the Duke's courtiers. Dolls and dolls – Celeste's dolls. Peachey's dolls, vacationing at Celeste's to visit their friends and relations. Killer didn't really like dolls, not even Dorothy, the most beautiful, with her long brown hair and bridal gown. She played with them, but they were not her friends. She preferred real things like babies and kittens and beach balls and toads and desserts.

Under Cissy's direction the Pretend went off perfectly. The arrival of the prince and his brothers was very exciting. With their invisible help, Elvira was tied and gagged and dragged off to prison. To make sure she would never again be free to plot against them, the three sisters and the three brothers placed pieces of cardboard (they had not told Killer this part) over the front and back entrances of the snow fort. These they covered with packed snow over which they dribbled a little boiling water. It froze almost immediately, making a nice smooth surface. Then they went off to the palace.

Of course they were not going to the palace. They were going to eat graham crackers with marshmallow and watch cartoons. They were going to tell Aunty Lil that Killer had run off to play with some children and didn't want her snack. They would be warm and giggling and eating her graham crackers. Afterwards they might take their sleds to McLin's field and have a snowball fight with the Dewhurst boys or go with them to the housing project and tip over the garbage cans.

Killer was cold and lonely. Her wet snow suit was no longer made warm by the heat of her body. They had tied her so tightly that she could not move. She looked round at her small prison of white. She could see, feel, hear the white, the whiteness of crazy nothing that scared her so much. She longed for Celeste and Cissy and Peachey. She wanted them to come and get her. She would play any game they liked, be any terrible person, she was so lonely here in the white.

They had walled her up with her accomplices in the plot – the three least loved of Celeste's dolls. They were no help. They had bad characters and did not care what became of her. Buster was a villain like she was – always trying to wreck plans, to spoil balls and ceremonies, to kidnap Dorothy. And June. June would do anything to attract men's attention. She was spiteful with short hair and told lies. She was also stupid and got the lowest marks at school. No one would ever marry June. Jackie, the dirty yellow and white rabbit, had been good at first when he arrived four years ago as an Easter Bunny. But he had allowed himself to be corrupted by Buster. Celeste said Jackie was a failure. His many crimes had made him unhappy, but it was too late for him to change his ways. Killer knew that she and Jackie and June and Buster were what Peachey's mother called Lost Souls.

Killer rubbed her tongue over her cold sore. It tasted like metal and tomatoes. She could never let it alone. Tomatoes made her think of last summer: picnics at Lake Acushnet, then fights in the car, after which she would cringe under the glare of Cissy's green eyes; Cissy and Peachey throwing jelly doughnuts at her and her throwing them back – the only time she had ever defended herself; Celeste covering her face with Ipana toothpaste in the middle of the night; Cissy and Celeste frightening her with ghost stories and tales of torture so that she lay quaking in the dark as she was quaking now in the white; Quaker Meetings on the lawn ('Quaker Meeting has begun, no more laughing, no more fun, if you show your teeth or tongue, you will have to pay a forfeit'); the Mermaid game on the beach and Cissy whipping her with one of those long flat strips of seaweed. 'Peachey, you may take one giant step. Killer, you may take one baby step.' Oh the games, the endless games she could not resist. She must always play, never say no, never complain, please them by letting them hate her and be afraid of her. It was such a funny thing. Why was it like that? She couldn't really understand Pretend. And Pretend was so important. Pretend was everything, because without it you were only yourself.

How come Cissy and Celeste could make things up? They could think so fast. If she could think fast too, she almost realized before her thoughts slid back into simply people and things and events, she might not have to be always The Crazy Doctor. Not only could Cissy and Peachey and Celeste think faster and eat faster and run faster; they seemed to need less sleep, less food, less love than she did. They seemed, with the exception of jelly doughnuts, not even to *want* any of those things. Killer longed for them. She longed for them now. But if she tried to get out of the snow fort before supper, they'd be sure to call her a spoilsport and to torment her all night long.

Better stay here a little longer and freeze. They would have to come back for her, because sooner or later they would need her for the games. They would not be able to have any of the good ones without her. She tried to feel very certain that they would come, but her heart was tightening, tightening and sinking. Her crime had been so terrible this time. No one could forgive her. Perhaps not even God could forgive her. She had broken the third commandment. She had killed the Duchess and tried to steal the inheritance. No, there was no chance of God forgiving her. He was going to let her freeze to death with Jackie and June and Buster, the Lost Souls. He would make the others forget her. He would make Aunty Lil and Uncle Raymond forget her, even her own mother and father probably. He *could* make everyone forget her. That kind of thing was easy for him. They probably had forgotten already. Or maybe it wasn't God at all. Maybe *they* wanted her to die, to freeze to death with Buster and June and Jackie. Get rid of the trouble-makers, the wicked ones, all at once. What about Mummy? She was always so kind, but that might be a Pretend too. She might really have been plotting with Cissy and the rest of them all along to wall up her little girl in a snow fort. Killer couldn't help it, she cried.

She cried until she had no more strength to cry. She began to give up, to fall asleep, to float away to a place where there was no more cold, where nothing was white, but all nice greens and reds and blues. Something was carrying her up to the sky, like Ragged Robin in the orange tree up and up, away from the white. It was Uncle Raymond. He was pulling her out of the snow fort, he was untying her, he was picking her up in his arms, taking her to the house, muttering over her.

'Oh my God, poor Killer.' She could not open her eyes, she was so tired. 'My God, poor little Killer.' She liked Uncle Raymond. He was a nice man.

The hospital where Killer spent the next two weeks was very white. When she first awoke, she was frightened and thought that the snow fort had grown larger and cleaner and more occupied. It was warm in the hospital (she saw quite quickly that it *was* a hospital) and there were lots of people, mainly kind, who leaned over her, gave her things, asked her questions in quiet tones, took things away, moved her about – sometimes hurting her, though not meaning to – and gazed at her for long stretches of time through her plastic tent. Their expressions were of worry, sorrow or silly cheerfulness, if grown-ups, and of questioning uncomfortableness, if children.

Killer hardly spoke. She *could* speak, she knew that, but she did not want to. She looked back through her plastic tent at all those queer expressions. Sometimes she smiled at them a little. Mostly she slept. Slept and dreamt. She dreamed they played the Mermaid game, and that she chased Cissy and Celeste and Peachey for ever along an empty beach.

When she was very much better, they took the plastic tent away and let the children come near her. Cissy's green eyes were still defiant, but she spoke nicely to her sister and called her Charlotte. Killer understood that Cissy and Celeste had had some kind of punishment, but that now everyone was pretending that nothing had ever really happened.

Peachey held her hand and leaned over her. 'Bests,' Peachey whispered. Killer blinked at her. Did she mean it, was she making believe? Killer didn't understand, but smiled to let Peachey know that she was pretending she did.

Celeste even offered her Dorothy to keep for ever and be her very own. Dorothy with her bridal gown and long brown hair.

Killer hesitated. Then she spoke for the first time since the day in the snow fort.

'Can I have June instead?' she asked.

Mary Flanagan

Working on White Places

1. The games we played

Think back to when you were six, seven or eight years old. To jog your memory, try to remember the names of some of your teachers and friends. Think about key events in your life around that time.
● Work in small groups. Share your memories of when you were that age, using the headings below to help you.

   – Best Friends
   – Clubs
   – Games we played
   – Bullies
   – Brothers and Sisters
   – Let's pretend ...
   – Nicknames

2. The beginning

'Killer was the youngest and the fattest.'

This sentence comes from the beginning of the story you are going to read.
● What expectations does it create for you?

3. Cissy revealed

● Stop reading at page 57, where Cissy begins to speak.
● Take turns in reading aloud Cissy's explanation of the game to the others. Try doing it like a speech in a play, experimenting with her voice, her facial expressions, her tone towards Killer and so on.
● After each of you has had a go at it, talk about what her speech shows about her personality and her relationship with Killer.

4. A child's world

The story is about little girls.
● Pick out three short extracts from the story that seem to you to give a real sense of how children think and feel. For each extract talk about:

– what aspects of childhood the writer is focusing on
– how true to life you find this
– how the writer creates a sense of how a child sees things

5. The dolls

On page 58 the dolls are described and the author says, 'Killer knew that she and Jackie and June and Buster were what Peachey's mother called Lost Souls.'
● What role do the dolls play in the children's lives? What do the dolls tell the reader about the children?

6. The ending

● Re-read the end from 'When she was very much better, they took the plastic tent away ...'
● Talk about what this ending seems to be saying about:

– whether anything has changed
– the way Killer sees herself and her world
– pretending
– the other children in the story

● Look closely at the last sentence of the story. What does it imply about Killer:

– that she is asserting herself against the other girls for the first time?
– that she has come to believe that she really is the villain that she has had to play in all their games?
– that nothing has really changed by the end of the story?
– that she will continue to be a victim in their games?

● What difference would it have made if Mary Flanagan had left the last sentence out?

7. The way the story is told

● Look at these quotes from the story and think about who is narrating the story and how the narrator allows us inside Killer's head. Your view might change from quote to quote. Is it:

– an adult voice, looking at the events with an adult's awareness?
– the voice of Killer?
– something in between the two?

> ‘Her name was not really Killer. It was Charlotte Mundy Fletcher Doyle (mixed marriage: Roman Catholic and Presbyterian.)’

> ‘Why the others liked pretending to be weak and frightened and in danger when really they were so strong, stronger than she would ever be, Killer could not understand.’

> 'Celeste's father and mother were very indulgent. Even when the girls kept them awake until four in the morning, they did not complain very much.'

> 'She thought she might like to go home. It would be nice to be tucked in by her mother and to watch her baby brother kicking his feet like a small fat bug, or dribbling breakfast down his pyjamas. But she was too scared to tell Aunty Lillian any of these things. Besides, she had to stay here and be a Body Snatcher.'

> '"But what about my graham crackers?" Killer knew she mustn't cry.'

> 'They were no help. They had bad characters and did not care what became of her. Buster was a villain like she was – always trying to wreck plans, to spoil balls and ceremonies, to kidnap Dorothy.'

> 'Better stay here a little longer and freeze.'

● Using ideas from your discussion of the quotes, as well as your ideas about the story as a whole, look at the list below and decide which of these things Mary Flanagan does in the story:

– gives us her views directly on what childhood is like
– describes each of the characters physically
– lets us know what the grown-ups think of what is going on
– ends her story with good conquering bad
– has a moral to the story
– captures what it *feels* like to be a small child
– is right about children and how they relate to each other and to adults

8. Your response to the story
● In small groups think about your responses to this story by choosing from this list the one statement that you feel describes it best:

– a chilling story
– a story about bullying
– a story that shows how children's problems are just as great as those faced by adults
– an attack on the idea that children are innocent
– a story about girls' relationships
– a psychologically interesting story

9. Ideas for writing

● Choose one memory or one topic heading from your small group discussion on memories, and make it the starting point for a piece of autobiographical writing.
● Choose one story that someone in your group has told. Make it the starting point for a *fictional* story of your own. Feel free to add details and change events or characters to make it a better story.
● Imagine that Killer, now grown up, writes the story in her own voice, as a first person narrative, looking back on the events during that winter. Write her narrative, thinking about how different it might be from Mary Flanagan's story. For instance, would she reflect on what childhood was like for her, from an adult point of view? Would she make judgements about Cissy, Peachey and Celeste? What would she have to say now about the games they played and about the adults in her life?

10. Comparative work – representations of childhood

Look at the suggestions for comparative work after the story, 'The Potato Gatherers'.

11. Comparative work – third person narratives

Look at the suggestions for comparative work after the story, 'A Small Good Thing'.

12. Wider reading suggestions

● Margaret Atwood's *Cat's Eye* is a novel about girls' friendships and how cruel girls can be towards each other. Atwood is a Canadian novelist.
● *I'm the King of the Castle* by Susan Hill is about bullying between two boys taken to terrifying extremes.
● *Blue Remembered Hills* by Dennis Potter is a play about a group of children where the bullying and victimisation of one of them goes horribly wrong.
● Alice Munro is a Canadian short story writer. Her collection *Dance of the Happy Shades* explores relationships in families, childhood feelings and the self-discovery of adolescence.
● The short stories in *A Bit of Singing and Dancing* by Susan Hill deal with some of the more disturbing and sinister sides of human behaviour.

Spirit

– Spirit 350?

– Yes.

– You died yesterday?

– Yes. Sunning myself in the garden.

– Quite so. Now if you'll rest from hovering I'll ask you a few questions, just a matter of form, you know, we are crowded here and like to find suitable eternal places for our clients. Now. What about your life? A brief outline perhaps.

– There's nothing much to say. The usual thing. Born in the South Island went to some kind of school learned writing and spelling and profit and loss and compositions My Holidays What I would most like to be when I grow up –

– What did you most want to be?

– Oh an inventor or explorer or sea captain.

– And were you?

– Oh no no of course not, these are just fancies we get when we are little kids running round the garden playing at being grown-ups. To tell you the truth I married early, Emily Barker.

– Emily Barker? Do you have names?

– Of course. I was Harry and there was my brother Dick and my sister Molly. Does that seem strange to you?'

– A little out of the ordinary perhaps. Go on.

– There's nothing much to say, as I told you before. We are creatures of habit. Lived in a little house, had four kids, worked at gardening, each day a round of eating and sleeping and other pleasures, pictures on the weekend, the bar on Friday nights at five for bar lunch, cold fish and dead potatoes, footy in the weekend, footy's a kind of game, every day mostly just going backwards and forwards doing this and that.

– I see, quite a simple existence. Any enemies?

– Yes we all have enemies. A big black death swoops down from the skies at any moment to carry us away. A kind of death got me yesterday while I was sunning myself in the garden. It's funny, and next year there will be the notice in the paper Sacred to the memory of, Gone but not forgotten.

– You have newspapers?

– Of course. And radio for the wrestling and the serials, and books too. And there's some sort of music and some of the folks paint and dance but give me three feeds a day and a comfortable place to live.

– You say there's music and dancing?

– Not for me. They're always trying to leave their mark on the world some sort of a trail but it's like the wind and the sand ha ha.

– Well, Spirit 350, I think that's all I want to know, if you just wait a moment I'll get you your eternal home. A nice permanently juicy leaf, quite small but comfortable.

– A leaf. A leaf. But I was a man. Men can't live on leaves.

– I'm sorry, I'll get your leaf. Nothing can be done now.

– But I tell you I was a human being, a man, 'in form and moving how like an angel' (they say). I've wept and laughed and fallen in love, I can remember and think, look at me thinking, I can think.

– Here is your leaf, Spirit 350. Aeons and aeons of juice here. You'll be alone of course but there'll be no swooping blackbirds to bother you. You may eat and sleep and slide up and down even making a little permanent silver patch of your own, and remember, no blackbirds to bother you.

Janet Frame

Working on Spirit

1. Life after death

● In small groups brainstorm ideas, views and information about what happens to people when they die. Is there a life after death? Where does it take place, how long for and what actually happens? What names do various cultures at different times give to the places people supposedly go to after death? What do we mean by the spirit or the soul?

2. Your own writing

● Try doing a short piece of imaginative writing describing one of the ideas about the after life discussed above. Write from the point of view of a spirit or soul and set your piece of writing in the place where they go after death.

To help you get started you should begin at the point at which a new spirit enters the after life. Keep it short; it's just a beginning.

● When everyone has written for about 10 minutes, read out your pieces to one another and then continue writing for 5 minutes more. How similar were people's ideas? Was the writing mainly humorous, serious or moving? Talk about why.

3. Reading 'Spirit'

This short story is a dialogue between two voices.
● Read it in pairs first and then get into fours to talk about your reactions to it. Think about the following:

Setting
– where does the story take place?
– can you describe what it looks like and what goes on there?

Themes and ideas
– what idea of life after death is the writer presenting here?
– how close or distant is it to the ideas you discussed before reading the story?
– make a list of all the questions this story poses

Style
– why is it written as a dialogue?
– talk about the two voices – who or what are they?
– what sort of dialogue is it?

– does it remind you of certain sorts of conversation on earth?
– what is the effect of this dialogue as a means of storytelling?
– how does it add to or reflect the story's ideas?

4. The ending

At the end of this story Spirit seems a little dissatisfied. What are the reasons for this?

● Talk about the following interpretations of the story and find evidence in the text to back up each one:

Spirit was a man when he was alive
Spirit was a worm when he was alive
Spirit was a worm but is pretending he was a man
In heaven all creatures are equal and therefore no better than worms
This is the story of a spirit that has gone to hell

5. Continue the story

● Explore the style and themes of 'Spirit' further by writing a continuation of the story.

Either write a further episode called 'Spirit 351' in which you reveal a little more of the place, the spirits, and the life they've left on earth,

or write a further episode in which Spirit 350 meets another spirit and they discuss what has happened.

6. Comparative work – death

'A Small Good Thing' by Raymond Carver is a very detailed and sustained look at the impact of death on three people. Grief is quite absent from 'Spirit'. Janet Frame's story is short and flippant, but do the two stories raise similar questions about life and death?

7. Comparative work – unusual ideas

Look at the suggestions for comparative work after the story, 'Along the River'.

8. Comparative work – other worlds

Look at the suggestions for comparative work after the short story, 'Headless'.

9. Comparative work – interesting narratives

Look at the suggestions for comparative work after the story 'Joe and America'.

10. Wider reading

● *The Lagoon and other stories* is the anthology by Janet Frame in which this story was originally published.
● *Sweetie* is a disturbing and often funny film adaptation of a Janet Frame story, directed by Jane Campion. It explores the family life of a schizophrenic girl.
● *An Angel at my Table* is an autobiographical novel by Janet Frame which has also been adapted as a film for TV.
● Samuel Beckett's 'Ping' is a highly unusual short story about life after death.

The Potato Gatherers

November frost had starched the flat countryside into silent rigidity. The 'rat-tat-tat' of the tractor's exhaust drilled into the clean, hard air but did not penetrate it; each staccato sound broke off as if it had been nipped. Hunched over the driver's wheel sat Kelly, the owner, a rock of a man with a huge head and broken fingernails, and in the trailer behind were his four potato gatherers – two young men, permanent farm hands, and the two boys he had hired for the day. At six o'clock in the morning, they were the only living things in that part of County Tyrone.

The boys chatted incessantly. They stood at the front of the trailer, legs apart, hands in their pockets, their faces pressed forward into the icy rush of air, their senses edged for perception. Joe, the elder of the two – he was thirteen and had worked for Kelly on two previous occasions – might have been quieter, but his brother's excitement was infectious. For this was Philly's first job, his first time to take a day off from school to earn money, his first opportunity to prove that he was a man at twelve years of age. His energy was a burden to him. Behind them, on the floor of the trailer, the two farm hands lay sprawled in half sleep.

Twice the boys had to cheer. The first time was when they were passing Dicey O'Donnell's house, and Philly, who was in the same class as Dicey, called across to the thatched, smokeless building, 'Remember me to all the boys, Dicey!' The second time was when they came to the school itself. It was then that Kelly turned to them and growled to them to shut up.

'Do you want the whole county to know you're taking the day off?' he said. 'Save your breath for your work.'

When Kelly faced back to the road ahead, Philly stuck his thumbs in his ears, put out his tongue, and wriggled his fingers at the back of Kelly's head. Then, suddenly forgetting him, he said, 'Tell me, Joe, what are you going to buy?'

'Buy?'

'With the money we get today. I know what I'm getting – a shotgun. Bang! Bang! Bang! Right there, mistah. Jist you put yer two hands up above yer head and I reckon you'll live a little longer.' He menaced Kelly's neck.

'Agh!' said Joe derisively.

'True as God, Joe. I can get it for seven shillings – an old one that's lying in Tom Tracy's father's barn. Tom told me he would sell it for seven shillings.'

'Who would sell it?'

'Tom.'

'Steal it, you mean. From his old fella.'

'His old fella has a new one. This one's not wanted.' He sighted along an imaginary barrel and picked out an unsuspecting sparrow in the hedge. 'Bang! Never knew what hit you, did you? What are you going to buy, Joe?'

'I don't know. There won't be much to buy with. Maybe – naw, I don't know. Depends on what Ma gives us back.'

'A bicycle, Joe. What about a bike? Quinn would give his away for a packet of cigarettes. You up on the saddle, Joe, and me on the crossbar. Out to the millrace every evening. Me shooting all the rabbits along the way. Bang! Bang! Bang! What about a bike, Joe?'

'I don't know. I don't know.'

'What did she give you back the last time?'

'I can't remember.'

'Ten shillings? More? What did you buy then? A leather belt? A set of rabbit snares?'

'I don't think I got anything back. Maybe a shilling. I don't remember.'

'A shilling! One lousy shilling out of fourteen! Do you know what I'm going to buy?' He hunched his shoulders and lowered his head between them. One eye closed in a huge wink. 'Tell no one? Promise?'

'What?'

'A gaff. See?'

'What about the gun?'

'It can wait until next year. But a gaff, Joe. See? Old Philly down there beside the Black Pool. A big salmon. A beaut. Flat on my belly, and – *phwist!* – there he is on the bank, the gaff stuck in his guts.' He clasped his middle and writhed in agony, imitating the fish. Then his act switched suddenly back to cowboys and he drew from both holsters at a cat sneaking home along the hedge. 'Bang! Bang! That sure settled you, boy. Where is this potato territory, mistah? Ah want to show you hombres what work is. What's a-keeping this old tractor-buggy?'

'We're jist about there, Mistah Philly, sir,' said Joe. 'Ah reckon you'll show us, OK. You'll show us.'

The field was a two-acre rectangle bordered by a low hedge. The ridges of potatoes stretched lengthwise in straight, black lines. Kelly unfastened the trailer and hooked up the mechanical digger. The two labourers stood with their hands in their pockets and scowled around them, cigarettes hanging from their lips.

'You two take the far side,' Kelly told them. 'And Joe, you and –' He could not remember the name. 'You and the lad there, you two take this side. You show him what to do, Joe. ' He climbed up on the tractor seat. 'And remember,' he called over his shoulder, 'if the school-attendance officer appears, it's up to you to run. I never seen you. I never heard of you.'

The tractor moved forward into the first ridges, throwing up a spray of brown earth behind it as it went.

'Right,' said Joe. 'What we do is this, Philly. When the digger passes, we gather the spuds into these buckets and then carry the buckets to the sacks and fill them. Then back again to fill the buckets. And back to the sacks. OK, mistah?'

'OK, mistah. Child's play. What does he want four of us for? I could do the whole field myself – one hand tied behind my back.'

Joe smiled at him. 'Come on, then. Let's see you.'

'Just you watch,' said Philly. He grabbed a bucket and ran stumbling across the broken ground. His small frame bent over the clay and his thin arms worked madly. Before Joe had begun gathering, Philly's voice called to him. 'Joe! Look! Full already! Not bad, eh?'

'Take your time,' Joe called back.

'And look, Joe! Look!' Philly held his hands out for his brother's inspection. They were coated with earth. 'How's that Joe? They'll soon be as hard as Kelly's!'

Joe laughed. 'Take it easy, Philly. No rush.'

But Philly was already stooped again over his work, and when Joe was emptying his first bucket into the sack, Philly was emptying his third. He gave Joe the huge wink again and raced off.

Kelly turned at the bottom of the field and came back up. Philly was standing waiting for him.

'What you need is a double digger, Mr Kelly!' he called as the tractor passed. But Kelly's eyes never left the ridges in front of him. A flock of seagulls swooped and dipped behind the tractor, fluttering down to catch worms in the newly-turned earth. The boy raced off with his bucket.

'How's it going?' shouted Joe after another twenty minutes. Philly was too busy to answer.

A pale sun appeared about eight-thirty. It was not strong enough to soften the earth, but it loosened sounds – cars along the road, birds in the naked trees, cattle let out for the day. The clay became damp under it but did not thaw. The tractor exulted in its new freedom and its splutterings filled the countryside.

'I've been thinking,' said Philly when he met Joe at a sack. 'Do you know what I'm going to get, Joe? A scout knife with one of those leather scabbards. Four shillings in Byrne's shop. Great for skinning a rabbit.' He held his hands out from his sides now, because they were raw in places. 'Yeah. A scout knife with a leather scabbard.'

'A scout knife,' Joe repeated.

'You always have to carry a scout knife in case your gun won't fire or your powder gets wet. And when you're swimming underwater, you can always carry a knife between your teeth.'

'We'll have near twenty ridges done before noon,' said Joe.

'He should have a double digger. I told him that. Too slow, mistah. Too doggone slow. Tell me, Joe, have you made up your mind yet?'

'What about?'

'What you're going to buy, stupid.'

'Aw, naw. Naw... I don't know yet.'

Philly turned to his work again and was about to begin, when the school bell rang. He dropped his bucket and danced back to his brother. 'Listen! Joe! Listen!' He caught fistfuls of his hair and tugged his head from side to side. 'Listen! Listen! Ha, ha, ha! Ho, ho, ho! Come on, you fat, silly, silly scholars and get to your lessons! Come on, come on, come on, come on! No dallying! Speed it up! Get a move on! Hurry! Hurry! Hurry! "And where are the O'Boyle brothers today? Eh? Where are they? Gathering potatoes? What's that I hear? What? What?" '

'Look out, lad!' roared Kelly.

The tractor passed within inches of Philly's legs. He jumped out of its way in time, but a fountain of clay fell on his head and shoulders. Joe ran to his side.

'Are you all right, Philly? Are you OK?'

'Tried to get me, that's what he did, the dirty cattle thief. Tried to get me.'

'You OK, mistah? Reckon you'll live?'

'Sure, mistah. Take more'n that ole coyote to scare me. Come on, mistah. We'll show him what men we really are.' He shook his jacket and hair and hitched up his trousers. 'Would you swap now, Joe?'

'Swap what?'

'Swap places with those poor eejits back there?' He jerked his thumb in the direction of the school.

'No sir,' said Joe. 'Not me.'

'Nor me neither, mistah. Meet you in the saloon.' He swaggered off, holding his hands as if they were delicate things, not part of him.

They broke for lunch at noon. By then, the sun was high and brave but still of little use. With the engine of the tractor cut off, for a brief time there was a self-conscious silence, which became relaxed and natural when the sparrows, now audible, began to chirp. The seagulls squabbled over the latest turned earth and a cautious puff of wind stirred the branches of the tall trees. Kelly adjusted the digger while he ate. On the far side of the field, the two labourers stretched themselves on sacks and conversed in monosyllables. Joe and Philly sat on upturned buckets. For lunch they each had half a scone of homemade soda bread, cut into thick slices and skimmed with butter. They washed it down with mouthfuls of cold tea from a bottle. After they had eaten, Joe threw the crusts to the gulls, gathered up the newspapers in which the bread had been wrapped, emptied out the remains of the tea, and put the bottle and the papers into his jacket pocket. Then he stood up and stretched himself.

'My back's getting stiff,' he said.

Philly sat with his elbows on his knees and studied the palms of his hands.

'Sore?' asked Joe.

'What?'

'Your hands. Are they hurting you?'

'They're OK,' said Philly. 'Tough as leather. But the clay's sore. Gets right into every cut and away up your nails.' He held his arms out. 'They're shaking,' he said. 'Look.'

'That's the way they go,' said Joe. 'But they'll – Listen! Do you hear?'

'Hear what?'

'Lunchtime at school. They must be playing football in the playground.'

The sounds of high, delighted squealing came intermittently when the wind sighed. They listened to it with their heads uplifted, their faces broadening with memory.

'We'll get a hammering tomorrow,' said Joe. 'Six on each hand.'

'It's going to be a scout knife,' Philly said. 'I've decided on that.'

'She mightn't give us anything back. Depends on how much she needs herself.'

'She said she would. She promised. Have you decided yet?'

'I'm still thinking,' said Joe.

The tractor roared suddenly, scattering every other sound.

'Come on, mistah,' said the older one. 'Four more hours to go. Saddle up your horse.'

'Coming. Coming,' Philly replied. His voice was sharp with irritation.

The sun was a failure. It held its position in the sky and flooded the countryside with light but could not warm it. Even before it had begun to slip to the west, the damp ground had become glossy again, and before the afternoon was spent, patches of white frost were appearing on higher ground. Now the boys were working automatically, their minds acquiescing in what their bodies did. They no longer straightened up; the world was their feet and the hard clay and the potatoes and their hands and the buckets and the sacks. Their ears told them where the tractor was, at the bottom of the field, turning, approaching. Their muscles had become adjusted to their stooped position, and as long as the boys kept within the established pattern of movement their arms and hands and legs and shoulders seemed to float as if they were free of gravity. But if something new was expected from the limbs – a piece of glass to be thrown into the hedge, a quick stepping back to avoid the digger – then their bodies shuddered with pain and the tall trees reeled and the hedges rose to the sky.

Dicey O'Donnell gave them a shout from the road on his way home from school. 'Hi! Joe! Philly!'

They did not hear him. He waited until the tractor turned. 'Hi! Hi! Philly! Philly! Joe!'

'Youse are for it the morrow. I'm telling youse. He knows where youse are. He says he's going to beat the scruff out of youse the morrow. Youse are in for it, all right. Blue murder! Bloody hell! True as God!'

'Get lost!' Joe called back.

'Aye, and he's going to report youse to the attendance officer, and your old fella'll be fined. Youse are ruined! Destroyed! Blue murder.'

'Will I put a bullet in him, mistah?' said Joe to Philly.

Philly did not answer. He thought he was going to fall, and his greatest fear was that he might fall in front of the tractor, because now the tractor's exhaust had only one sound, fixed forever in his head, and unless he saw the machine he could not tell whether it was near him or far away. The 'rat-tat-tat' was a finger tapping in his head, drumming at the back of his eyes.

'Vamoose, O'Donnell!' called Joe. 'You annoy us. Vamoose.'

O'Donnell said something more about the reception they could expect the next day, but he got tired of calling to two stooped backs and he went off home.

The last pair of ridges was turned when the sky had veiled itself for dusk. The two brothers and the two labourers worked on until they met in the middle. Now the field was all brown, all flat, except for the filled sacks that patterned it. Kelly was satisfied; his lips formed an O and he blew through them as if he were trying to whistle. He detached the digger and hooked up the trailer. 'All aboard!' he shouted, in an effort at levity.

On the way home the labourers seemed to be fully awake, for the first time since morning. They stood in the trailer where the boys had stood at dawn, behind Kelly's head and facing the road before them. They chatted and guffawed and made plans for a dance that night. When they met people they knew along the way, they saluted extravagantly. At the crossroads, they began to wrestle, and Kelly had to tell them to watch out or they would fall over the side. But he did not sound angry.

Joe sat on the floor, his legs straight out before him, his back resting against the side of the trailer. Philly lay flat out, his head cushioned on his brother's lap. Above him, the sky spread out, grey, motionless, enigmatic. The warmth from Joe's body made him drowsy. He wished the journey home to go on forever, the sound of the tractor engine to anaesthetize his mind forever. He knew that if the movement and the sound were to cease, the pain of his body would be unbearable.

'We're nearly there,' said Joe quietly. 'Are you asleep?' Philly did not answer. 'Mistah! Are you asleep, mistah?'

'No.'

Darkness came quickly, and when the last trace of light disappeared the countryside became taut with frost. The headlamps of the tractor glowed yellow in the cold air.

'Philly? Are you awake, mistah?'

'What?'

'I've been thinking,' said Joe slowly. 'And do you know what I think? I think I've made up my mind now.'

One of the labourers burst into song.

'If I were a blackbird, I'd whistle and sing, and I'd follow the ship that my true love sails in.'

His mate joined him at the second line and their voices exploded in the stiff night.

'Do you know what I'm going to buy?' Joe said, speaking more loudly. 'If she gives us something back, that is. Mistah! Mistah Philly! Are you listening? I'm going to buy a pair of red silk socks.'

He waited for approval from Philly. When none came, he reshook his brother's head. 'Do you hear, mistah? Red silk socks – the kind Jojo Teague wears. What about that, eh? What do you think?'

Philly stirred and half-raised his head from his brother's lap. 'I think you're daft,' he said in an exhausted, sullen voice. 'Ma won't give us back enough to buy anything much. No more than a shilling. You knew it all the time.' He lay down again and in a moment he was fast asleep.

Joe held his brother's head against the motion of the trailer and repeated the words 'red silk socks' to himself again and again, nodding each time at the wisdom of his decision.

Brian Friel

Working on The Potato Gatherers

1. The shape of the story:

The events	The school day	The changing feel-ings/behaviour of the boys and men
Journey out to the fields	Passing the school	
Starting work	The school bell rings	
Lunchtime	Lunchtime at school	
The afternoon	School ends – Dicey O'Donnell sees them	
Journey home		

● Make a chart like the one above, tracing the feelings and behaviour of Philly, Joe and the labourers at each of these stages in the story.
● Why do you think the writer keeps mentioning what's happening at school?
● The writer describes the sun at different moments in the day. Look for these moments. What do the descriptions of the sun add to the story?

2. The setting
● How would you describe the setting of the story?
How does the writer create a sense of the places in the story?
If the story were set somewhere else, what difference would it make?
Are the feelings in the story recognisable, wherever you come from?

3. Boys and men
For Philly his first day of work seems to signal the beginning of his manhood.
● Go through the story looking for examples of him trying to assert his male identity. Make a list of the examples and try to say something about each one.
● The story focuses on the two boys and their relationship. Make a list of adjectives you could use to describe the boys and the way they relate to each other.
Find three or four short quotes that would support the adjectives you have chosen.

4. Ideas for writing

● Continue the story when the boys get home to their mother and what happens to them the next day at school.
● Re-tell the events of the day from the point of view of one of the adults, either Kelly or one of the labourers. What might they think about Philly's changing behaviour during the day? You could write it as the thoughts of that character, or perhaps as a dialogue between the two labourers in the bar that evening.
● If you have had a part-time job, write about your own first day at work, or about an incident at your work.

5. Comparative work – representations of childhood

● Look at the relationship between the two brothers. Compare it with the relationship between Cissy and Killer in 'White Places' and write about the different representations of childhood in the two stories.
You might think about:

– the way the children talk and behave towards each other
– their feelings about each other and about other aspects of their lives, such as adults, parents etc.
– what aspect of their lives the stories focus on
– what view of childhood is suggested
– how the writer has developed the idea of the story, e.g. through dialogue, using suspense or tension, a child's eye view, drawing a moral at the end, using description of people and places etc.
– how important the Irish and American contexts are to the stories

6. Comparative work – young people

Look at the suggestions for comparative work after the story 'Kreativ Riting'.

7. Wider reading

● Brian Friel's stories in *Selected Stories* are all set in the north western counties of Ireland. He is also very well known as a playwright. His play, *Translations*, is sometimes studied at A Level.
● James Joyce's stories *Dubliners* create a picture of ordinary people's lives in Dublin at the beginning of the century.
● *Paddy Clarke Ha Ha Ha* [GCSE] by Roddy Doyle is written from the point of view of an 11 year old boy growing up in Dublin. A lot of the story is told in dialogue and it is both funny and tragic.
● Bernard McClaverty's novel *Cal* is a powerful story of adolescence in Ireland. His short stories, *The Best of Bernard MacLaverty* (Windmill) explore painful or embarassing moments in young people's lives.
● Pat Barker's *The Man Who Wasn't There* is a novel about an 11 year old boy, preoccupied with trying to find out about his absent father.
● [GCSE] Seamus Heaney has written many poems about his childhood in rural Ireland, including 'Digging', 'At a Potato Digging', 'Cow in Calf', 'Follower' and 'The Early Purges'. Like Friel he gives a strong sense of country life, of family and of the loss of childhood illusions.

My Son the Fanatic

Surreptitiously, the father began going into his son's bedroom. He would sit there for hours, rousing himself only to seek clues. What bewildered him was that Ali was getting tidier. The room, which was usually a tangle of clothes, books, cricket bats and video games, was becoming neat and ordered; spaces began appearing where before there had been only mess.

Initially, Parvez had been pleased: his son was outgrowing his teenage attitudes. But one day, beside the dustbin, Parvez found a torn shopping bag that contained not only old toys but computer disks, videotapes, new books, and fashionable clothes the boy had bought a few months before. Also without explanation, Ali had parted from the English girlfriend who used to come around to the house. His old friends stopped ringing.

For reasons he didn't himself understand, Parvez was unable to bring up the subject of Ali's unusual behaviour. He was aware that he had become slightly afraid of his son, who, between his silences, was developing a sharp tongue. One remark Parvez did make – 'You don't play your guitar anymore' – elicited the mysterious but conclusive reply, 'There are more important things to be done.'

Yet Parvez felt his son's eccentricity as an injustice. He had always been aware of the pitfalls that other men's sons had stumbled into in England. It was for Ali that Parvez worked long hours; he spent a lot of money paying for Ali's education as an accountant. He had bought Ali good suits, all the books he required, and a computer. And now the boy was throwing his possessions out! The TV, video-player and stereo system followed the guitar. Soon the room was practically bare. Even the unhappy walls bore pale marks where Ali's pictures had been removed.

Parvez couldn't sleep; he went more often to the whisky bottle, even when he was at work. He realised it was imperative to discuss the matter with someone sympathetic.

Parvez had been a taxi-driver for twenty years. Half that time he'd worked for the same firm. Like him, most of the other drivers were Punjabis. They preferred to work at night, when the roads were clearer and the money better. They slept during the day, avoiding their wives. They led almost a boy's life together in the cabbies' office, playing cards and setting up practical jokes, exchanging lewd stories, eating takeaways from local *balti* houses, and discussing politics and their own problems.

But Parvez had been unable to discuss the subject of Ali with his friends. He was too ashamed. And he was afraid, too, that they would blame him for the wrong turning his boy had taken, just as he had blamed other fathers whose sons began running around with bad girls, skipping school and joining gangs.

For years, Parvez had boasted to the other men about how Ali excelled in cricket, swimming and football, and what an attentive scholar he was, getting As in most subjects. Was it asking too much for Ali to get a good job, marry the right girl, and start a family? Once this happened, Parvez would be happy. His dreams of doing well in England would have come true. Where had he gone wrong?

One night, sitting in the taxi office on busted chairs with his two closest friends, watching a Sylvester Stallone film, Parvez broke his silence.

'I can't understand it!' he burst out. 'Everything is going from his room. And I can't talk to him any more. We were not father and son – we were brothers. Where has he gone? Why is he torturing me?' And Parvez put his head in his hands.

Even as he poured out his account, the men shook their heads and gave one another knowing glances.

'Tell me what is happening!' he demanded.

The reply was almost triumphant. They had guessed something was going wrong. Now it was clear: Ali was taking drugs and selling his possessions to pay for them. That was why his bedroom was being emptied.

'What must I do, then?'

Parvez's friends instructed him to watch Ali scrupulously and to be severe with him, before the boy went mad, overdosed, or murdered someone.

Parvez staggered out into the early-morning air, terrified that they were right. His boy – the drug-addict killer!

To his relief, he found Bettina sitting in his car.

Usually the last customers of the night were local 'brasses', or prostitutes. The taxi-drivers knew them well and often drove them to liaisons. At the end of the girls' night, the men would ferry them home, though sometimes they would join the cabbies for a drinking session in the office. Occasionally, the drivers would go with the girls. 'A ride in exchange for a ride,' it was called.

Bettina had known Parvez for three years. She lived outside the town and, on the long drives home, during which she sat not in the passenger seat but beside him, Parvez had talked to her about his life and hopes, just as she talked about hers. They saw each other most nights.

He could talk to her about things he'd never be able to discuss with his own wife. Bettina, in turn, always reported on her night's activities. He liked to know where she had been and with whom. Once, he had rescued her from a violent client, and since then they had come to care for each other.

Though Bettina had never met Ali, she heard about the boy continually. That night, when Parvez told Bettina that he suspected Ali was on drugs, to Parvez's relief, she judged neither him nor the boy, but said, 'It's all in the eyes.' They might be bloodshot; the pupils might be dilated; Ali might look tired. He could be liable to sweats, or sudden mood changes. 'OK?'

Parvez began his vigil gratefully. Now that he knew what the problem might be, he felt better. And surely, he figured, things couldn't have gone too far?

He watched each mouthful the boy took. He sat beside him at every opportunity and looked into his eyes. When he could, he took the boy's hand, checked his temperature. If the boy wasn't at home, Parvez was active, looking under the carpet, in Ali's drawers, and behind the empty wardrobe sniffing, inspecting, probing. He knew what to look for: Bettina had drawn pictures of capsules, syringes, pills, powders, rocks.

Every night, she waited to hear news of what he'd witnessed. After a few days of constant observation, Parvez was able to report that although the boy had given up sports, he seemed healthy. His eyes were clear. He didn't as Parvez expected he might– flinch guiltily from his father's gaze. In fact, the boy seemed more alert and steady than usual: as well as being sullen, he was very watchful. He returned his father's long looks with more than a hint of criticism, of reproach, even – so much so that Parvez began to feel that it was he who was in the wrong, and not the boy.

'And there's nothing else physically different?' Bettina asked.

'No!' Parvez thought for a moment. 'But he is growing a beard.'

One night, after sitting with Bettina in an all-night coffee shop, Parvez came home particularly late. Reluctantly, he and Bettina had abandoned the drug theory, for Parvez had found nothing resembling any drug in Ali's room. Besides, Ali wasn't selling his belongings. He threw them out, gave them away, or donated them to charity shops.

Standing in the hall, Parvez heard the boy's alarm clock go off. Parvez hurried into his bedroom, where his wife, still awake, was sewing in bed. He ordered her to sit down and keep quiet, though she had neither stood up nor said a word. As she watched him curiously, he observed his son through the crack of the door.

The boy went into the bathroom to wash. When he returned to his room, Parvez sprang across the hall and set his ear to Ali's door. A muttering sound came from within. Parvez was puzzled but relieved.

Once this clue had been established, Parvez watched him at other times. The boy was praying. Without fail, when he was at home, he prayed five times a day.

Parvez had grown up in Lahore, where all young boys had been taught the Koran. To stop Parvez from falling asleep while he studied, the *maulvi* had attached a piece of string to the ceiling and tied it to Parvez's hair, so if his head fell forward, he would instantly jerk awake. After this indignity, Parvez had avoided all religions. Not that the other taxidrivers had any more respect than he. In fact, they made jokes about the local mullahs walking around with their caps and beards, thinking they could tell people how to live while their eyes roved over the boys and girls in their care.

Parvez described to Bettina what he had discovered. He informed the men in the taxi office. His friends, who had been so inquisitive before, now became oddly silent. They could hardly condemn the boy for his devotions.

Parvez decided to take a night off and go out with the boy. They could talk things over. He wanted to hear how things were going at college; he wanted to tell him stories about their family in Pakistan. More than anything, he seemed to understand how Ali had discovered the 'spiritual dimension', as Bettina called it.

To Parvez's surprise, the boy refused to accompany him. He claimed he had an appointment. Parvez had to insist that no appointment could be more important than that of a son with his father.

The next day, Parvez went immediately to the street corner where Bettina stood in the rain wearing high heels, a short skirt, and a long mac, which she would open hopefully at passing cars.

'Get in, get in!' he said.

They drove out across the moors and parked at the spot where, on better days, their view unimpeded for miles except by wild deer and horses, they'd lie back, with their eyes half-closed, saying, 'This is the life.' This time Parvez was trembling. Bettina put her arms around him.

'What's happened?'

'I've just had the worst experience of my life.'

As Bettina rubbed his head Parvez told her that the previous evening, as he and his son had studied the menu, the waiter, whom Parvez knew, brought him his usual whisky-and-water. Parvez was so nervous he had even prepared a question. He was going to ask Ali if he was worried about his imminent exams. But first he loosened his tie, crunched a poppadum, and took a long drink.

Before Parvez could speak, Ali made a face.

'Don't you know it's wrong to drink alcohol?' he had said.

'He spoke to me very harshly,' Parvez said to Bettina. 'I was about to castigate the boy for being insolent, but I managed to control myself.'

Parvez had explained patiently that for years he had worked more than ten hours a day, had few enjoyments or hobbies, and never gone on holiday. Surely it wasn't a crime to have a drink when he wanted one?

'But it is forbidden,' the boy said.

Parvez shrugged. 'I know.'

'And so is gambling, isn't it?'

'Yes. But surely we are only human?'

Each time Parvez took a drink, the boy winced, or made some kind of fastidious face. This made Parvez drink more quickly. The waiter, wanting to please his friend, brought another glass of whisky. Parvez knew he was getting drunk, but he couldn't stop himself. Ali had a horrible look, full of disgust and censure. It was as if he hated his father.

Halfway through the meal, Parvez suddenly lost his temper and threw a plate on the floor. He felt like ripping the cloth from the table, but the waiters and other customers were staring at him. Yet he wouldn't stand for his own son's telling him the difference between right and wrong. He knew he wasn't a bad man. He had a conscience. There were a few things of which he was ashamed, but on the whole he had lived a decent life.

'When have I had time to be wicked?' he asked Ali.

In a low, monotonous voice, the boy explained that Parvez had not, in fact, lived a good life. He had broken countless rules of the Koran.

'For instance?' Parvez demanded.

Ali didn't need to think. As if he had been waiting for this moment, he asked his father if he didn't relish pork pies?

'Well.' Parvez couldn't deny that he loved crispy bacon smothered with mushrooms and mustard and sandwiched between slices of fried bread. In fact, he ate this for breakfast every morning.

Ali then reminded Parvez that he had ordered his wife to cook pork sausages, saying to her, 'You're not in the village now. This is England. We have to fit in.'

Parvez was so annoyed and perplexed by this attack that he called for more drink.

'The problem is this,' the boy said. He leaned across the table. For the first time that night, his eyes were alive. 'You are too implicated in Western civilisation.'

Parvez burped; he thought he was going to choke. 'Implicated!' he said. 'But we live here!'

'The Western materialists hate us,' Ali said. 'Papa, how can you love something which hates you?'

'What is the answer, then,' Parvez said miserably, 'according to you?'

Ali didn't need to think. He addressed his father fluently, as if Parvez were a rowdy crowd which had to be quelled or convinced. The law of Islam would rule the world; the skin of the infidel would burn off again and again; the Jews and Christers would be routed. The West was a sink of hypocrites, adulterers, homosexuals, drug users and prostitutes.

While Ali talked, Parvez looked out the window as if to check that they were still in London.

'My people have taken enough. If the persecution doesn't stop, there will be jihad. I, and millions of others, will gladly give our lives for the cause.'

'But why, why?' Parvez said.

'For us, the reward will be in Paradise.'

'Paradise!'

Finally, as Parvez's eyes filled with tears, the boy urged him to mend his ways.

'But how would that be possible?' Parvez asked.

'Pray,' urged Ali. 'Pray beside me.'

Parvez paid the bill and ushered his boy out of there as soon as he was able. He couldn't take any more.

Ali sounded as if he'd swallowed someone else's voice.

On the way home, the boy sat in the back of the taxi, as if he were a customer. 'What has made you like this?' Parvez asked him, afraid that somehow he was to blame for all this.

'Is there a particular event which has influenced you?'

'Living in this country.'

'But I love England,' Parvez said, watching his boy in the rear view mirror. 'They let you do almost anything here.'

'That is the problem,' Ali replied.

For the first time in years, Parvez couldn't see straight. He knocked the side of the car against a lorry, ripping off the wing mirror. They were lucky not to have been stopped by the police: Parvez would have lost his licence and his job.

Back at the house, as he got out of the car, Parvez stumbled and fell in the road, scraping his hands and ripping his trousers. He managed to haul himself up. The boy didn't even offer him his hand.

Parvez told Bettina he was willing to pray, if that was what the boy wanted – if it would dislodge the pitiless look from his eyes. 'But what I object to,' he said, 'is being told by my own son that I am going to Hell!'

What had finished Parvez off was the boy's saying he was giving up his studies in accounting. When Parvez had asked why, Ali said sarcastically that it was obvious. 'Western education cultivates an anti-religious attitude.'

And in the world of accountants it was usual to meet women, drink alcohol, and practise usury.

'But it's well-paid work,' Parvez argued. 'For years you've been preparing!'

Ali said he was going to begin to work in prisons, with poor Muslims who were struggling to maintain their purity in the face of corruption. Finally, at the end of the evening, as Ali went up to bed, he had asked his father why he didn't have a beard, or at least a moustache.

'I feel as if I've lost my son,' Parvez told Bettina. 'I can't bear to be looked at as if I'm a criminal. I've decided what to do.'

'What is it?'

'I'm going to tell him to pick up his prayer mat and get out of my house. It will be the hardest thing I've ever done, but tonight I'm going to do it.'

'But you mustn't give up on him,' said Bettina. 'Many young people fall into cults and superstitious groups. It doesn't mean they'll always feel the same way.' She said Parvez had to stick by his boy.

Parvez was persuaded that she was right, even though he didn't feel like giving his son more love when he had hardly been thanked for all he had already given.

For the next two weeks, Parvez tried to endure his son's looks and reproaches. He attempted to make conversation about Ali's beliefs. But if Parvez ventured any criticism, Ali always had a brusque reply. On one occasion, Ali accused Parvez of 'grovelling' to the whites; in contrast, he explained, he himself was not 'inferior'; there was more to the world than the West, though the West always thought it was best.

'How is it you know that?' Parvez said. 'Seeing as you've never left England?'

Ali replied with a look of contempt.

One night, having ensured there was no alcohol on his breath, Parvez sat down at the kitchen table with Ali. He hoped Ali would compliment him on the beard he was growing, but Ali didn't appear to notice it.

The previous day, Parvez had been telling Bettina that he thought people in the West sometimes felt inwardly empty and that people needed a philosophy to live by.

'Yes,' Bettina had said. 'That's the answer. You must tell him what your philosophy of life is. Then he will understand that there are other beliefs.'

After some fatiguing consideration, Parvez was ready to begin. The boy watched him as if he expected nothing. Haltingly, Parvez said that people had to treat one another with respect, particularly children their parents. This did seem, for a moment, to affect the boy. Heartened, Parvez continued. In his view, this life was all there was, and when you died, you rotted in the earth. 'Grass and flowers will grow out of my grave, but something of me will live on.'

'How then?'

'In other people. For instance, I will continue in you.'

At this the boy appeared a little distressed.

'And in your grandchildren,' Parvez added for good measure. 'But while I am here on earth I want to make the best of it. And I want you to, as well!'

'What d'you mean by "make the best of it"?' asked the boy.

'Well,' said Parvez. 'For a start... you should enjoy yourself. Yes. Enjoy yourself without hurting others.'

Ali said enjoyment was 'a bottomless pit'.

'But I don't mean enjoyment like that,' said Parvez. 'I mean the beauty of living.'

'All over the world our people are oppressed,' was the boy's reply.

'I know,' Parvez answered, not entirely sure who 'our people' were. 'But still – life is for living!'

Ali said, 'Real morality has existed for hundreds of years. Around the world millions and millions of people share my beliefs. Are you saying you are right and they are all wrong?' And Ali looked at his father with such aggressive confidence that Parvez would say no more.

A few evenings later, Bettina was riding in Parvez's car after visiting a client when they passed a boy on the street.

'That's my son,' Parvez said, his face set hard. They were on the other side of town, in a poor district, where there were two mosques.

Bettina turned to see. 'Slow down, then, slow down!'

She said, 'He's good-looking. Reminds me of you. But with a more determined face. Please, can't we stop?'

'What for?'

'I'd like to talk to him.'

Parvez turned the cab round and pulled up beside the boy.

'Coming home?' Parvez asked. 'It's quite a way.'

The boy shrugged and got into the back seat. Bettina sat in the front. Parvez became aware of Bettina's short skirt, her gaudy rings and ice-blue eyeshadow. He became conscious that the smell of her perfume, which he loved, filled the cab. He opened the window.

While Parvez drove as fast as he could, Bettina said gently to Ali, 'Where have you been?'

'The mosque,' he said.

'And how are you getting on at college? Are you working hard?'

'Who are you to ask me these questions?' Ali said, looking out of the window. Then they hit bad traffic, and the car came to a standstill.

By now, Bettina had inadvertently laid her hand on Parvez's shoulder. She said, 'Your father, who is a good man, is very worried about you. You know he loves you more than his own life.'

'You say he loves me,' the boy said.

'Yes!' said Bettina.

'Then why is he letting a woman like you touch him like that?'

If Bettina looked at the boy in anger, he looked back at her with cold fury.

She said, 'What kind of woman am I that I should deserve to be spoken to like that?'

'You know what kind,' he said. Then he turned to his father. 'Now let me out.'

'Never,' Parvez replied.

'Don't worry, I'm getting out,' Bettina said.

'No, don't!' said Parvez. But even as the car moved forward, she opened the door and threw herself out – she had done this before – and ran away across the road. Parvez stopped and shouted after her several times, but she had gone.

Parvez took Ali back to the house, saying nothing more to him. Ali went straight to his room. Parvez was unable to read the paper, watch television, or even sit down. He kept pouring himself drinks.

At last, he went upstairs and paced up and down outside Ali's room. When, finally, he opened the door, Ali was praying. The boy didn't even glance his way.

Parvez kicked him over. Then he dragged the boy up by the front of his shirt and hit him. The boy fell back. Parvez hit him again. The boy's face was bloody. Parvez was panting; he knew the boy was unreachable, but he struck him none the less. The boy neither covered himself nor retaliated; there was no fear in his eyes. He only said, through his split lip, 'So who's the fanatic now?'

Hanif Kureishi

Working on My Son the Fanatic

Before reading

1. Father and son role-play

In this story a father is angry with his teenage son.

● In small groups talk about some of the situations that commonly lead to conflict between fathers and teenage sons. In pairs prepare a short scene to show one of these situations as a role-play.

Role-play debrief:

● What do these role-plays show us about the behaviour and characteristics of fathers and sons at this time during their relationship?

● Would the arguments have been different if the father had been a mother? Are mother and daughter conflicts different?

● What are some of the solutions to the problems explored in the role-plays?

After reading

2. First reactions

● In pairs or small groups talk about your reactions to and feelings about this story as soon as you've finished reading it. What are your experiences and opinions of the issues that it raises?

3. The writer's characterisation of Parvez and Ali

● Look at the quotes listed below about Parvez, and for each one note down what it adds to our understanding of the character.

Parvez

> 'Surreptitiously, the father began going into his son's bedroom ...'

> 'He was aware that he had become slightly afraid of his son ...'

> 'It was for Ali that Parvez worked long hours ...'

86

'They led almost a boy's life together in the cabbies' office ...'

'Parvez had boasted to the other men about how Ali had excelled in cricket ...'

'He could talk to her about things he would never be able to discuss with his wife ...'

'Parvez knew he was getting drunk but he couldn't stop himself ...'

'This is England. We have to fit in ...'

'he knew the boy was unreachable, but he struck him none the less ...'

- Now collect some quotes for Ali and then compare lists.
- Do you think the writer of this story has more sympathy for Parvez or for Ali? How can you tell?

4. Funny or serious?
This story contains a balance of humour and serious messages and ideas.
- Look back through it and draw up two lists to give examples of Hanif Kureishi's use of humour and seriousness in the story.
- Talk about why you think he has chosen to do this.

5. What if ...?
- What intentions and motives lie behind some of the decisions Hanif Kureishi makes in the writing of this story? How might this story have been different if some of those decisions were reversed? Discuss the following possibilities and their effects on the story as a whole:

- what if Parvez had been less extreme in his own behaviour?
- what if the ending hadn't been there?
- what if Bettina the prostitute hadn't been in the story?
- what if Parvez had been a very religious man himself?
- what if Ali's mother had been a more prominent character in the story?
- what if Parvez had discovered that Ali was taking drugs?

6. A TV adaptation
- Imagine that you have been asked to adapt this story into a half-hour TV drama. Prepare a detailed proposal for a treatment of the story, to 'sell' your ideas for the

adaptation to a Commissioning Editor on a TV channel of your choice. Look back to the media task for 'A Small Good Thing' on page 52, which suggests some issues to think about in preparing a treatment. Consider the following issues before you start:

– from whose point of view will the story be told?
– the story deals with difficult issues about religion and culture. What concerns might TV executives have about tackling these sensitive areas? How would your adaptation deal with them?
– what sorts of audiences might be interested in this story and how would you dramatise the story to appeal to them?
– what sorts of changes might you need to make to the story to create effective television drama?
– what sorts of changes might you need to make to ensure that you do not offend any particular segment of the community?

• 'My Son the Fanatic' is currently being adapted as a BBC film. You may want to watch it and compare it with your own proposed treatment.

7. Comparative work – choosing a culture
Look at the suggestions for comparative work after the story 'The Two Grandmothers'.

8. Comparative work – young people
Look at the suggestions for comparative work after the story 'Kreativ Riting'.

9. Wider reading
• Hanif Kureishi's novel *The Buddha of Suburbia* was adapted as a TV drama. He also wrote the screenplay for the film *My Beautiful Laundrette*. His latest novel, *The Black Album* is about a young student at college. The story explores the experience of living in two very different cultures.
• *Sumitra's Story* by Rukshana Smith deals with a young girl's experience of moving from Uganda to London in the 1970s, and the cultural conflicts that arise for her.
• *Oranges are Not the Only Fruit* by Jeanette Winterson is set in Lancashire. It is about a girl who rebels against her family's evangelical Christianity and rigid values. It is a powerful, at time funny, short autobiographical novel.

Along the River

The mdambres used to lay eggs and let the sun hatch them. Often the eggs got addled, or eaten by eefoots, and if they did hatch out, the hatchlings had to bring themselves up, and so had no conversation or manners at all. But when the mdambres learned how to make their children out of clay and bake them, it changed everything.

They had to make the children very carefully, and keep the oven fires at the right temperature, watching day and night, cooking the children little by little, so that they would learn how to come alive, how to move, and eat, and sleep, and speak. In doing all this, the mdambres became proficient in the social arts. That was when they started to call themselves mdambres, which means 'people' in their language.

The mdambres with flippers and big teeth could light fire by biting flint with their teeth, and they were good at chewing down trees. Their flippers were useful for building big things like ovens, though not so good at shaping little figures out of clay. So they cut the wood and built the fires under the ovens. The mdambres with fingers and toes were better at shaping clay, so they made the children and watched them cook, turning and basting them and making sure they didn't burn, while the others watched the fires. So the ones with fingers and toes called themselves the cooks, and the ones with flippers and big teeth called themselves the firelighters.

It only took one firelighter to light a fire and keep it burning. The firelighters had spare time, and all mdambres like making things out of clay, so they went on and built mudbrick kitchens for the ovens to be in, and houses for the kitchens to be in, and dikes and walls around the houses to keep out the floods of the river and the incursions of eefoots. They went on that way, the firelighters building and the cooks cooking, and nobody bothered to lay eggs any more. Pretty soon the baked ones were the only kind of mdambre. They made their children and baked them, taught them manners, protected them with walls, fished and cut wood and tended the gardens, and enjoyed sex and conversation, as is the way of people.

The careful work of making and baking the children took a lot of the cooks' time. It seemed like they were always in the kitchen. Back when the mdambres laid eggs nobody ever had much to do except fish and chew trees and putter in the garden, but things were different now.

The firelighters kept the fires burning, and also kept on making houses and dikes and walls, always larger and finer. One would build a tower onto the house; a neighbor would build a taller tower; then they would throw mud at each other from the windows, shouting jokes and insults. Or one would build a wall around a garden and others would come knock it down with their flippers, shouting that that was their garden. Or one would chew down a lot of trees for the oven-fires and float the logs down the river and build a big woodpile, and then another would get even more wood and build a bigger woodpile. Pretty soon the forests along that part of the river were getting thin, and it was easier to steal wood than go chew down trees. The firelighters had to keep watch in the towers and drive thieves away from the woodpiles by throwing balls of mud at them. After a while all the firelighters went around armed with mudballs. All the houses had tall towers and all the towns had huge woodpiles and high walls.

The firelighters had always been the best swimmers and caught the most fish. The cooks had always been better at gardening than fishing, and these days they hardly fished at all any more, being busy making and baking children. Besides, they had to keep the children away from the river. Young children who were still raw or halfbaked couldn't swim. In the water they would turn back to mud. But they could help the cooks tend the gardens, and the firelighters did the fishing. It all worked out fine.

In one mdambre town the firelighter who had the most dried fish in the biggest house with the tallest tower announced that she was the chief. The other firelighters agreed. Then the chief came to the kitchens with all the other firelighters and said to the cooks, 'Make more children with flippers and big teeth.'

'Why?'

'We want more baby firelighters.'

'What for?'

'To fish, to cut wood, to build walls against the enemy, to fight in the mudball wars, and to light the sacred fires.'

'There are plenty of people to cut wood and light fires,' said the cooks, 'and we have enough walls, plenty of fish, and too many mudballs.'

'You do not understand,' said the chief firelighter. 'You're busy all day long doing nothing but baking children, tending gardens, cleaning things, and talking. You do not live in the great world. You do not understand what is important.'

At this the cooks were puzzled. They talked together, as is the way of people.

'They must know what's important, since they're out of town a lot, swimming up and down the river, and have time to make so many mudballs and throw them at each other,' said a female cook.

'But what's important about that?' asked a male cook.

'Well, everybody needs work to do,' said an old cook.

'But I want to make my first child with fingers,' said a young cook, 'so it can help in the garden, and bake grandchildren for me. Then I'll make the next one a firelighter to fish for us.'

'What is a chief, and why is this chief person telling us what to do?' asked another.

All the cooks asked the firelighters, 'Why are you telling us what to do instead of talking together with us, as is the way of people?'

When the chief and the other firelighters heard that they got angry. They roared. They came into the kitchen and put out the fires of the ovens. They beat the cooks with their flippers and bit them with their big teeth till they bled. They took the halfbaked children and broke them into pieces. They threw the raw baby cooks into the river, where they turned to mudstains in the water. 'You cannot cook unless we light the fires!' they shouted.

And when a cook tried to relight the fire by rubbing two sticks together, they broke the sticks and his fingers with their flippers.

Since then the towers of the chiefs of the mdambres have grown to be the wonder of the riverbank. Their towns are great and marvelous, full of the stink of drying fish.

The firelighters are very large and strong, because the cooks make them so. They make them with huge flippers that can build mighty walls and towers and hurl mudballs with deadly force. They bake and rebake them till they are hard as stone. All the eefoots along that part of the river have been killed. All the forests are gone, and wood for the fires must be floated down the river from the mountains. All the mdambre towns are at war because they raid each other for wood. The largest, strongest firelighters are warriors.

The cooks make themselves small. They make themselves with fine fingers, good at making and baking children, gardening, cleaning houses, healing wounds, and the other things that, like conversation and manners, the mdambres consider unimportant.

Once a cook made a very large, very strong baby cook. As soon as they saw it the firelighters made a law against large, strong cooks. The chiefs had discovered that although they could not make children, they could make laws, and did not even need ovens for them. The new law said that large, strong baby cooks were illegitimate. The illegitimate baby was thrown in the river and turned to a stain of brown mud in the water. The cook that made it was executed by mudball. Many cooks helped the firelighters throw the mudballs, because it was the law, and they believed that only their firelighters could protect them from their many enemies in the great world outside the kitchen.

Only the ones with flippers are called mdambres, now. The ones with hands and the children who aren't baked yet are called cookies.

Ursula Le Guin

Working on Along the River

1. Expectations
● Look at this sentence and discuss it using the questions that follow to help you.

'The mdambres used to lay eggs and let the sun hatch them ...'

– what sort of writing is this going to be?
– what's it going to be about?
– does it remind you of anything you have read or seen before?

● Try writing the next few sentences in the same style. Listen to one another's short pieces. What kind of creatures are the mdambres?

2. Predictions
● Here is an extract from the story you are going to read. Talk about the ideas and possible situations it suggests to you.

'You're busy all day long doing nothing but baking children, tending gardens, cleaning things, and talking. You do not live in the great world. You do not understand what is important.'

3. Your first reactions to this story
● When you have finished reading the story, talk about your responses to it. Look back at your 'Before reading' notes. How far were the ideas you had then developed in the story?

4. Ideas and questions about the story
Although this story is short and uses quite simple language it is dealing with some difficult ideas. Getting to grips with the meaning will require a lot of close reading, questioning and talk.
● In your groups, complete the following sentence and then tell the rest of the class what you have written.

One thing we think this story is about is ....
but **one question** we want answered is ....

● Select one or two questions put by other groups and set about finding an answer to them by looking closely at the story.

5. Firelighters and cooks
● Make two lists to show all the ways in which the firelighters are different from the cooks.

6. Baking children?
● In small groups, brainstorm all the words and ideas you can think of to do with baking.
● Feed back to the other groups with one reason why you think the writer has used this idea in her story.
● As a whole class talk about what the story says about the way that children are brought up.

7. Stages in mdambre history
● Imagine you are researching mdambre history and development. Alongside the main stages in their history, find a suitable quote from the story and add a few notes about their behaviour and lifestyle.

Stages in mdambre history	Behaviour, lifestyles etc.
egg laying creatures	'the hatchlings had to bring themselves up' – no language, offspring left to fend for themselves
discovered fire	
built villages	
wood becomes scarce and valuable	
local chiefs establish themselves	
conflict between firelighters and cooks	
cooks become cookies, firelighters become chiefs	

8. Style and purpose
● Which of the following dictionary definitions best describes the way that this story has been written and the reasons for writing it in this way? Annotate each definition to show which features appear in 'Along the River.' The first one has been done for you, as an example.

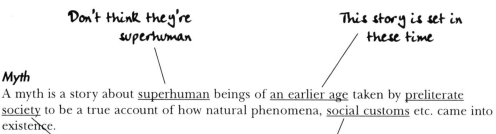

Myth
A myth is a story about <u>superhuman</u> beings of <u>an earlier age</u> taken by <u>preliterate society</u> to be a true account of how natural phenomena, <u>social customs</u> etc. came into existence.

Don't think they're superhuman

This story is set in these time

This story was written recently for our society

It does seem to be explaining social customs

Allegory
An allegory is a poem, play, picture etc. in which the apparent meaning of the characters and events is used to symbolise a deeper moral or spiritual meaning.

Science fiction
A literary genre that makes imaginative use of scientific knowledge or conjecture.

Fable
A short moral story, especially one with animals as characters.

9. What is this story about?
● Look at the following suggestions, and under each one list quotes from the story to back it up. You may want to add a suggestion of your own.
This story is about:

– the evolution of human beings
– the destruction of the environment
– the difference between people and animals
– the differences between people
– conflict between males and females
– the way power is used and abused
– family life
– why women are smaller than men

10. Comparative work – unusual ideas
'Spirit' is another very short story which takes an idea and explores it in an unusual way. In both stories the writer makes the reader work very hard, firstly to understand what is going on and then to grapple with the ideas in the story.
● Write about your experiences of reading these stories, your initial expectations or assumptions, the difficulties and pleasures involved, and any interesting similarities or differences you can see between them. You might consider the way the two stories open and close, their structure, the relationship set up between the writer and the reader in the story, and the narrative voice used.

11. Wider reading

● Ursula Le Guin's novel *City of Illusions* uses science fiction to raise issues about the nature of our world.

● William Golding's *The Inheritors* is a novel about early humankind, set before the discovery of fire.

● 'A Jury of her Peers' by Susan Glaspell, in the English & Media Centre publication *Reading Stories*, is a short story which explores conflict between the sexes.

● 'Manhood' by John Wain, also in *Reading Stories*, is a short story which explores gender differences in the way we raise children.

● Margaret Atwood's novel *The Handmaid's Tale* deals with gender roles in society by imagining a future nightmare world.

● Charlotte Perkins Gilman's *Herland* is a utopia of an all-female world, written in the early twentieth century.

Joebell and America

ONE

Joebell find that he seeing too much hell in Trinidad so he make up his mind to leave and go away. The place he find he should go is America, where everybody have a motor car and you could ski on snow and where it have seventy-five channels of colour television that never sign off and you could sit down and watch for days, all the boxing and wrestling and basketball, right there as it happening. Money is the one problem that keeping him in Cunaripo; but that year as Christmas was coming, luck hit Joebell in the gamble, and for three days straight he win out the wappie. After he give two good pardners a stake and hand his mother a raise and buy a watch for his girl, he still have nineteen hundred and seventy-five Trinidad and Tobago dollars that is his own. That was the time. If Joebell don't go to America now, he will never go again.

But, a couple years earlier, Joebell make prison for a wounding, and before that they had him up for resisting arrest and using obscene language. Joebell have a record; and for him to get a passport he must first get a letter from the police to say that he is of good character. All the bribe Joebell try to bribe, he can't get this letter from the police. He prepare to pay a thousand dollars for the letter; but the police pardner who he had working on the matter keep telling him to come back and come back and come back. But another pardner tell him that with the same thousand dollars he could get a whole new American passport, with new name and everything. The only thing a little ticklish is Joebell will have to talk Yankee.

Joebell smile, because if is one gift he have it is to talk languages, not Spanish and French and Italian and such, but he could talk English and American and Grenadian and Jamaican; and of all of them the one he love best is American. If that is the only problem, well, Joebell in America already.

But it have another problem. The fellar who fixing up the passport business for him tell him straight, if he try to go direct from Trinidad to America with the US passport, he could get arrest at the Trinidad airport, so the pardner advise that the best thing to do is for Joebell to try to get in through Puerto Rico where they have all those Spanish people and where the immigration don't be so fussy. Matter fix. Joebell write another pardner who he went to school with and who in the States seven years, and tell him he coming over, to look out for him, he will ring him from Puerto Rico.

Up in Independence Recreation Club where we gamble, since Joebell win this big money, he is a hero. All the fellars is suddenly his friend, everybody calling out, 'Joebell! Joebell!' some asking his opinion and some giving him advice on how to gamble his money. But Joebell not in no hurry. He know just as how you could win fast playing wappie, so you could lose fast too; and, although he want to stay in the wappie room and hear how we talk up his gambling ability, he decide that the safer thing to do is to go and play poker where if he have to lose he could lose more slow and where if he lucky he could win a good raise too. Joebell don't really have to be in the gambling club at all. His money is his own; but Joebell have himself down as a hero, and to win and run away is not classy. Joebell have himself down as classy.

Fellars' eyes open big big that night when they see Joebell heading for the poker room, because in there it have Japan and Fisherman from Mayaro and Captain and Papoye and a fellar named Morgan who every Thursday does come up from Tunapuna with a paper bag full with money and a knife in his shoe. Every man in there could real play poker.

In wappie, luck is the master; but in poker skill is what make luck work for you. When day break that Friday morning, Joebell stagger out the poker room with his whole body wash down with perspiration, out five hundred of his good dollars. Friday night he come back with the money he had give his girl to keep. By eleven he was down three. Fellars get silent and all of us vex to see how money he wait so long to get he giving away so easy. But, Joebell was really to go America in truth. In the middle of the poker, he leave the game to pee. On his way back, he walk into the wappie room. If you see Joebell: the whole front of his shirt open and wiping sweat from all behind his head. 'Heat!' somebody laugh and say. On the table that time is two card: Jack and Trey. Albon and Ram was winning everybody. The both of them like Trey. They gobbling up all bets. Was a Friday night. Waterworks get pay, County Council get pay. It had men from Forestry. It had fellars from the Housing Project. Money high high on the table. Joebell favourite card is Jack.

Ram was a loser the night Joebell win big; now, Ram on top.

'Who against trey?' Ram say. He don't look at Joebell, but everybody know is Joebell he talking to. Out of all Joebell money, one thousand gone to pay for the false passport, and, already in the poker he lose eight. Joebell have himself down as a hero. A hero can't turn away. Everybody waiting to see. They talking, but, they waiting to see what Joebell will do. Joebell wipe his face, then wipe his chest, then he wring out the perspiration from the handkerchief, fold the kerchief and put it round his neck, and bam, just like that, like how you see in pictures when the star boy, quiet all the time, begin to make his move, Joebell crawl right up the wappie table, fellars clearing the way for him, and, everything, he empty out everything he had in his two pocket, and, lazy lazy, like he really is that star boy, he say, 'Jack for this money!'

Ram was waiting, 'Count it, Casa,' Ram say.

When they count the money was two hundred and thirteen dollars and some change. Joebell throw the change for a broken hustler, Ram match him. Bam! Bam! Bam! In three card, Jack play.

'Double!' Joebell say. 'For all,' which mean that Joebell betting that another Jack play before any Trey.

Ram put some, and Albon put the rest, they sure is robbery.

Whap! Whap! Whap! Jack play. 'Devine!' Joebell say. That night Joebell leave the club with fifteen hundred dollars. Fellars calling him The Gambler of Natchez.

When we see Joebell next, his beard shave off, his head cut in a GI trim, and he walking with a fast kinda shuffle, his body leaned forward and his hands in his pockets and he talking Yankee: 'How ya doin, Main! Hi-ya, Baby!' And then we don't see Joebell in Cunaripo.

'Joebell gone away,' his mother, Miss Myrtle say, 'Praise God!'

If they have to give a medal for patience in Cunaripo, Miss Myrtle believe that the medal is hers just from the trials and tribulations she undergo with Joebell. Since he leave school his best friend is Trouble and wherever Trouble is, right there is Joebell.

'I shoulda mind my child myself,' she complain. 'His grandmother spoil him too much, make him feel he is too much of a star, make him believe that the world too easy.'

'The world don't owe you anything, boy,' she tell him. 'Try to be decent, son,' she say. Is like a stick break in Joebell two ears, he don't hear a word she have to say. She talk to him. She ask his uncle Floyd to talk to him. She go by the priest in Mount St Benedict to say a novena for him. She say the ninety-first psalm for him. She go by a *obeah* woman in Moruga to see what really happening to him. The *obeah* woman tell her to bring him quick so she could give him a bath and a guard to keep off the evil spirit that somebody have lighting on him. Joebell fly up in one big vexation with his mother for enticing him to go to the *obeah* woman: 'Ma, what stupidness you trying to get me in? You know I don't believe in the negromancy business. What blight you want to fall on me now? That is why it so hard for me to win in gamble, you crossing up my luck.'

But Miss Myrtle pray and she pray and at last, praise God, the answer come, not as how she did want it – you can't get everything the way you want it – but, praise God, Joebell gone away. And to those that close to her, she whisper, 'America!' for that is the destination Joebell give her.

But Joebell aint reach America yet. His girl Alicia, who working at Last Chance snackette on the Cunaripo road is the only one he tell that Puerto Rico is the place he trying to get to. Since she take up with Joebell, her mother quarrelling with her every day, 'How a nice girl like you could get in with such a vagabond fellar? You don't have eyes in your head to see that the boy is only trouble?' They talk to her, they tell her how he stab a man in the gambling club and went to jail. They tell her how he have this ugly beard on his face and this ugly look in his face. They tell her how he don't work nowhere regular, 'Child, why you bringing this cross into your life?' they ask her. They get her Uncle Matthew to talk to her. They carry her to Mount St Benedict for the priest to say a novena for her. They give her the ninety-first psalm to say. They carry her to Moruga to a *obeah* woman who bathe her in a tub with bush, and smoke incense all over her to untangle her mind from Joebell.

But there is a style about Joebell that she like. Is a dream in him that she see. And a sad craziness that make her sad too but in a happy kinda way. The first time she see him in the snackette, she watch him and don't say nothing but, she think, Hey! who he think he is? He come in the snackette with this foolish grin on his face and this strolling walk and this kinda commanding way about him and sit down at the table with his legs wide open, taking up a big space as if he spending a hundred dollars, and all he ask for is a coconut roll and a juice. And then he call her again, this time he want a napkin and a toothpick. Napkins and toothpicks is for people who eating food; but she give them to him. And still he sit down there with some blight, some trouble hanging over him, looking for somebody to quarrel with or for something to get him vex so he could parade. She just do her work, and not a word she tell him. And just like that, just so by himself he cool down and start talking to her though they didn't introduce.

Everything he talk about is big: big mountains and big cars and race horses and heavyweight boxing champions and people in America – everything big. And she look at him from behind the counter and she see his sad craziness and she hear him talk about all this bigness far away, that make her feel too that she would like to go somewhere and be somebody, and just like that, without any words, or touching it begin.

Sometimes he'd come in the snackette, walking big and singing, and those times he'd be so broke all he could afford to call for'd be a glass of cold water. He wanted to be a calypsonian, he say; but he didn't have no great tune and his compositions wasn't so great either and everything he sing had a kinda sadness about it, no matter how he sing it. Before they start talking direct to one another he'd sing, closing his eyes and hunching his shoulders, and people in the snackette'd think he was just making joke; but, she know the song was for her and she'd feel pretty and sad and think about places far away. He used to sing in a country and western style, this song: his own composition:

Gonna take ma baby
Away on a trip
Gonna take ma baby
Yip yip yip
We gonna travel far
To New Orleans
Me and ma baby
Be digging the scene

If somebody came in and had to be served, he'd stop singing while she served them, then he'd start up again. And just so, without saying anything or touching or anything, she was his girl.

She never tell him about the trouble she was getting at home because of him. In fact she hardly talk at all. She'd just sit there behind the counter and listen to him. He had another calypso that he thought would be a hit.

> Look at Mahatma Ghandi
> Look at Hitler and Mussolini
> Look at Uriah Butler
> Look at Kwame Nkrumah
> Great as they was
> Everyone of them had to stand the pressure

He used to take up the paper that was on one side of the counter and sit down and read it, 'Derby day,' he would say. 'Look at the horses running,' and he would read out the horses' names. Or it would be boxing, and he would say Muhammed boxing today, or Sugar. He talked about these people as if they were personal friends of his. One day he brought her five pounds of deer wrapped in a big brown paper bag. She was sure he pay a lot of money for it. 'Put this in the fridge until you going home.' Chenette, mangoes, oranges, sapodillas, he was always bringing things for her. When her mother ask her where she was getting these things, she tell her that the owner of the place give them to her. For her birthday Joebell bring her a big box wrapped in fancy paper and went away, so proud and shy, he couldn't stand to see her open it, and when she open it it was a vase with a whole bunch of flowers made from coloured feathers and a big birthday card with an inscription: From guess who?

'Now, who give you this? The owner?' her mother asked.

She had to make up another story.

When he was broke she would slip him a dollar or two of her own money and if he win in the gamble he would give her some of the money to keep for him, but she didn't keep it long, he mostly always came back for it next day. And they didn't have to say anything to understand each other. He would just watch her and she would know from his face if he was broke and want a dollar or if he just drop in to see her, and he could tell from her face if she want him to stay away altogether that day or if he should make a turn and come again or what. He didn't get to go no place with her, cause in the night when the snackette close her big brother would be waiting to take her home.

'Thank God!' her mother say when she hear Joebell gone away. 'Thank you, Master Jesus, for helping to deliver this child from the clutches of that vagabond.' She was so happy she hold a thanksgiving feast, buy sweet drinks and make cake and invite all the neighbours' little children; and she was surprise that Alicia was smiling. But Alicia was thinking, Lord, just please let him get to America, they will see who is vagabond. Lord, just let him get through that immigration they will see happiness when he send for me.

The fellars go round by the snackette where Alicia working and they ask for Joebell.

'Joebell gone away,' she tell them.

'Gone away and leave a nice girl like you? If was me I would never leave you.'

And she just smile that smile that make her look like she crying and she mumble something that don't mean nothing, but if you listen good is, 'Well, is not you.'

'Why you don't let me take you to the dance in the Centre Saturday? Joey Lewis playing. Why you don't come and forget that crazy fellar?'

But Alicia smile no, all the time thinking, wait until he send for me, you will see who crazy. And she sell the cake and the coconut roll and sweet drink and mauby that they ask for and take their money and give them their change and move off with that soft, bright, drowsy sadness that stir fellars, that make them sit down and drink their sweet drink and eat their coconut roll and look at her face with the spread of her nose and the lips stretch across her mouth in a full round soft curve and her far away eyes and think how lucky Joebell is.

When Joebell get the passport he look at the picture in it and he say, 'Wait! This fellar aint look like me. A blind man could see this is not me.'

'I know you woulda say that,' the pardner with the passport say, 'You could see you don't know nothing about the American immigration. Listen, in America, every black face is the same to white people. They don't see no difference. And this fellar here is the same height as you, roughly the same age. That is what you have to think about, those little details, not how his face looking.' That was his pardner talking.

'You saying this is me, this fellar here is me?' Joebell ask again. 'You want them to lock me up or what, man? This is what I pay a thousand dollars for? A lock up?'

'Look, you have no worry. I went America one time on a passport where the fellar had a beard and I was shave clean and they aint question me. If you was white you mighta have a problem, but black, man, you easy.'

And in truth when he think of it, Joebell could see the point, cause he aint sure he could tell the difference between two Chinese.

'But, wait!' Joebell say, 'Suppose I meet up a black immigration?'

'Ah!' the fellar say, 'You thinking. Anyhow, it aint have that many, but, if you see one stay far from him.'

So Joebell, with his passport in his pocket, get a fellar who running contraband to carry him to Venezuela where his brother was living. He decide to spend a couple days by his brother and from there take a plane to Puerto Rico, in transit to America.

His brother had a job as a motor car mechanic.

'Why you don't stay here?' his brother tell him, 'It have work here you could get. And TV does be on whole day.'

'The TV in Spanish,' Joebell tell him.

'You could learn Spanish.'

'By the time I finish learn Spanish I is a old man, 'Joebell say, ' *Caramba! Caramba! Habla! Habla!* No. And besides I done pay my thousand dollars. I have my American passport. I is an American citizen. And,' he whisper, softening just at the thought of her, 'I have a girl who coming to meet me in America.'

Joebell leave Venezuela in a brown suit that he get from his brother, a strong-looking pair of brown leather boots that he buy, with buckles instead of laces, a cowboy hat on his head and an old camera from his brother over his shoulder and in his mouth is a cigar, and now he is James Armstrong Brady of the one hundred and twenty-fifth infantry regiment from Alabama, Vietnam Veteran, twenty-six years old. And when he reach the airport in Puerto Rico he walk with a stagger and he puff his cigar like he already home in the United States of America. And not for one moment it don't strike Joebell that he doing any wrong.

No. Joebell believe the whole world is a hustle. He believe everybody running some game, putting on some show and the only thing that separate people is that some have power and others don't have none, that who in in and who out out, and that is exactly what Joebell kick against, because Joebell have himself down as a hero too and he not prepare to sit down timid timid as if he stupid and see a set of bluffers take over the world, and he stay wasting away in Cunaripo; and that is Joebell's trouble. That is what people call his craziness, is that that mark him out. That is the 'light' that the *obeah* woman in Moruga see burning on him, is that that frighten his mother and charm Alicia and make her mother want to pry her loose from him. Is that that fellars see when they see him throw down his last hundred dollars on a single card, as if he know it going to play. The thing is that Joebell really don't be betting on the card, Joebell does be betting on himself. He don't be trying to guess about which card is the right one, he is trying to find that power in himself that will make him call correct. And that power is what Joebell searching for as he queue up in the line leading to the immigration entering Puerto Rico. Is that power that he calling up in himself as he stand there, because if he can feel that power, if that power come inside him, then, nothing could stop him. And now this was it.

'Mr Brady?' The immigration man look up from Joebell passport and say, same time turning the leaves of the passport. And he glance at Joebell and he look at the picture. And he take up another book and look in it, and look again at Joebell; and maybe it is that power Joebell reaching for, that thing inside him, his craziness that look like arrogance, that put a kinda sneer on his face that make the immigration fellar take another look.

'Vietnam Veteran? Mr Brady, where you coming from?'

'Venezuela.'

The fellar ask a few more questions. He is asking Joebell more questions than he ask anybody.

'Whatsamatta? Watsa problem?' Joebell ask, 'Man, I aint never seen such incompetency as you got here. This is boring. Hey, I've got a plane to catch. I aint got all day.'

All in the airport people looking at Joebell 'cause Joebell not talking easy, and he biting his cigar so that his words coming to the immigration through his teeth. Why Joebell get on so is because Joebell believe that one of the main marks of a real American is that he don't stand no nonsense. Any time you get a real American in an aggravating situation, the first thing he do is let his voice be heard in objection: in other words, he does get on. In fact that is one of the things Joebell admire most about Americans: they like to get on. They don't care who hear them, they going to open their mouth and talk for their rights. So that is why Joebell get on so about incompetency and missing his plane and so on. Most fellars who didn't know what it was to be a real American woulda take it cool. Joebell know what he doing.

'Sir, please step into the first room on your right and take a seat until your name is called.' Now is the immigration talking, and the fellar firm and he not frighten, 'cause he is American too. I don't know if Joebell didn't realise that before he get on. That is the kind of miscalculation Joebell does make sometimes in gambling and in life.

'Maan, just you remember I gotta plane to catch,' and Joebell step off, with that slow, tall insolence like Jack Palance getting off his horse in *Shane,* but he take off his hat and go and sit down where the fellar tell him to sit down.

It had seven other people in the room but Joebell go and sit down alone by himself because with all the talk he talking big, Joebell just playing for time, just trying to put them off; and now he start figuring serious how he going to get through this one. And he feeling for that power, that craziness that sometimes take him over when he in a wappie game, when every bet he call he call right; and he telling himself they can't trap him with any question because he grow up in America right there in Trinidad. In his grandmother days was the British; but he know from Al Jolson to James Brown. He know Tallahashie bridge and Rocktow mountain. He know Doris Day and Frank Sinatra. He know America. And Joebell settle himself down not bothering to remember anything, just calling up his power. And then he see this tall black fellar over six foot five enter the room. At a glance Joebell could tell he's a crook, and next thing he know is this fellar coming to sit down side of him.

TWO

I sit down there by myself alone and I know they watching me. Everybody else in the room white. This black fellar come in the room, with beads of perspiration running down his face and his eyes wild and he looking round like he escape. As soon as I see him I say 'Oh God!' because I know with all the empty seats all about the place is me he coming to. He don't know my troubles. He believe I want friends. I want to tell him 'Listen, man, I love you. I really dig my people, but now is not the time to come and talk to me. Go and be friendly by those other people, they could afford to be friends with you.' But I can't tell him that 'cause I don't want to offend him and I have to watch how I talking in case in my situation I slip from American to Trinidadian. He shake my hand in the Black Power sign. And we sit down there side by side, two crooks, he and me, unless he's a spy they send to spy on me.

I letting him do all the talking, I just nodding and saying yeah, yeah.

He's an American who just come out of jail in Puerto Rico for dope or something. He was in Vietnam too. He talking, but I really aint listening to him.

I thinking how my plane going. I thinking about Alicia and how sad her face will get when she don't get the letter that I suppose to send for her to come to America. I thinking about my mother and about the fellars up in Independence Recreation Club and around the wappie table when the betting slow, how they will talk about me, 'Natchez', who win in the wappie and go to America – nobody ever do that before – and I thinking how nice it will be for me and Alicia after we spend some time in America to go back home to Trinidad for a holiday and stay in the Hilton and hire a big car and go to see her mother. I think about the Spanish I woulda have to learn if I did stay in Venezuela.

At last they call me inside another room. This time I go cool. It have two fellars in this room, a big tough one with a stone face and a jaw like a steel trap, and a small brisk one with eyes like a squirrel. The small one is smoking a cigarette. The tough one is the one asking questions. The small one just sit down there with his squirrel eyes watching me, and smoking his cigarette.

'What's your name?'

And I watching his jaw how they clamping down on the words. 'Ma name is James Armstrong Brady.'

'Age?'

And he go through a whole long set of questions.

'You're a Vietnam Veteran, you say? Where did you train?'

And I smile 'cause I see enough war pictures to know, 'Nor' Carolina,' I say.

'Went to school there?'

I tell him where I went to school. He ask questions until I dizzy.

The both of them know I lying, and maybe they coulda just throw me in jail just so without no big interrogation; but, America. That is why I love America. They love a challenge. Something in my style is a challenge to them, and they just don't want to lock me up because they have the power, they want to trap me plain for even me to see. So now is me, Joebell, and these two Yankees. And I waiting, 'cause I grow up on John Wayne and Gary Cooper and Audie Murphy and James Stewart and Jeff Chandler. I know the Dodgers and Phillies, the Redskins and the Dallas Cowboys, Green Bay Packers and the Vikings. I know Walt Frazier and Doctor J, and Bill Russell and Wilt Chamberlain. Really, in truth, I know America so much, I feel American. Is just that I aint born there.

As fast as the squirrel-eye one finish smoke one cigarette, he light another one. He aint saying nothing, only listening. At last he put out his cigarette, he say, 'Recite the alphabet.'

'Say what?'

'The alphabet. Recite it.'

And just so I know I get catch. The question too easy. Too easy like a calm blue sea. And, pardner, I look at that sea and I think about Alicia and the warm soft curving sadness of her lips and her eyes full with crying, make me feel to cry for me and Alicia and Trinidad and America and I know like when you make a bet you see a certain card play that it will be a miracle if the card you bet on play. I lose, I know. But I is still a hero. I can't bluff forever. I have myself down as classy. And, really, I wasn't frighten for nothing, not for nothing, wasn't afraid of jail or of poverty or of Puerto Rico or America and I wasn't vex with the fellar who sell me the passport for the thousand dollars, nor with Iron Jaw and Squirrel Eyes. In fact, I kinda respect them. 'A... B... C... ' And Squirrel Eyes take out another cigarette and don't light it, just keep knocking it against the pack, Tock! Tock! Tock! K... L... M... And I feel I love Alicia... V... W... and I hear Paul Robeson sing 'Old Man River' and I see Sammy Davis Junior dance Mr Bojangle's dance and I hear Nina Simone humming humming 'Suzanne', and I love Alicia; and I hear Harry Belafonte's rasping call, 'Daay-o, Daaay-o! Daylight come and me want to go home,' and Aretha Franklyn screaming screaming, '... Y... Zed.'

'Bastard!' the squirrel eyes cry out, 'Got you!'

And straightaway from another door two police weighed down with all their keys and their handcuffs and their pistols and their night stick and torch light enter and clink their handcuffs on my hands. They catch me. God! And now, how to go? I think about getting on like an American, but I never see an American lose. I think about making a performance like the British, steady, stiff upper lip like Alec Guinness in *The Bridge over the River Kwai*, but with my hat and my boots and my piece of cigar, that didn't match, so I say I might as well take my losses like a West Indian, like a Trinidadian. I decide to sing. It was the classiest thing that ever pass through Puerto Rico airport, me with these handcuffs on, walking between these two police and singing,

> Gonna take ma baby
> Away on a trip
> Gonna take ma baby
> Yip yip yip
> We gonna travel far
> To New Orleans
> Me and ma Baby
> Be digging the scene

Earl Lovelace

Working on Joebell and America

1. American dreams

'Joebell find that he seeing too much hell in Trinidad so he make up his mind to leave and go away. The place he find he should go is America ...'

The dream of emigrating to America has been a powerful force in many third world countries, where poverty and small-town life seem to offer little hope and America beckons as a land of opportunity. Joebell, the hero of this story, lives in Cunaripo, a small town in Trinidad, an island in the Caribbean.

● Talk about what images of America Joebell might have. Where might his view of America come from? Why would he choose America rather than anywhere else?

2. Putting together the story

There are lots of different episodes, or strands, each of which contributes to the story.

● Choose one moment that you particularly enjoyed, using the list below to help you:

– Joebell and the passport
– the poker game
– Miss Myrtle and Joebell
– Alicia and Joebell
– Alicia after Joebell leaves
– Joebell in Venezuela
– Joebell and the immigration officers

● Think carefully about what you think this particular episode contributes to the story (e.g. humour, suspense, telling us more about Joebell, making the reader feel pity or admiration for Joebell, moving the story on, creating the atmosphere of Cunaripo etc.).

● Think about how Lovelace has crafted this episode or strand. What works particularly well for you in the way it is written?

● Present your ideas about this part of the story to the rest of the class.

3. Hero, villain or something else?

The narrator says of his main character, 'Joebell have himself down as a hero.'

● What kind of hero is Joebell? In talking about this, consider these issues:

– what kind of hero does he see himself as? Who does he model himself on?
– who else thinks of him as a hero? Does anyone disagree?
– what is the attitude of the narrator to him? What does he want the reader to think of Joebell?
– is Joebell a hero in the end?
– what do you think the writer is saying about men like Joebell?
– what do you think the writer is saying through his character about Trinidad and America?

4. Two narrators

Lovelace chose to break the narrative into two parts.
● Why do you think he made this choice? How does it affect the way the reader responds to Joebell and to the end of the story?
● Look closely at who narrates each part. For part one, is it a completely distant detached third person narrator or someone with a relationship with Joebell? What difference does this make?
● Experiment with re-writing the opening of part one in Joebell's voice and the opening of part two as a third person narration. When you have finished, think about what difference it makes.

5. The language of the story

The story is told in a mixture of standard and non-standard Trinidadian – not just the dialogue, but the whole story.
● Experiment with re-writing the first paragraph in standard English. What effect does this have?
● Why do you think Lovelace made the language choices that he did for both the dialogue *and* the narrative? What effect does this have on how close or distant the narrator is to Joebell and the other characters?

6. Cunaripo hears about Joebell

● Imagine that you are one of the other characters in the story, who hears that Joebell has failed to gain entry to America. Write about your views on the events of the story and your feelings about Joebell, bearing in mind the likely attitudes of your chosen character. For instance, Miss Myrtle or Alicia's mother would have a different perspective to one of Joebell's 'pardners' or Alicia herself.

7. Comparative work – American dreams

The story 'American Dreams', by Peter Carey is also about people living in a small town and wanting to escape to America.
● Compare the two stories by looking closely at:

– who each story is about and whose eyes you see it through
– how the small town community and the key characters are evoked by each writer
– what each story seems to be saying about dreams of escape
– what kind of narrator is used in each story and in what ways
– what interesting techniques and uses of language each writer employs in crafting the story.

8. Comparative work – interesting narratives

'Joebell and America' is unusual in having two different narrators. 'Spirit' by Janet Frame, and 'The Two Grandmothers' by Olive Senior also use unusual methods of narration.

● Compare the three stories, focusing particularly on what makes them interesting in terms of the ways in which they are narrated.

9. Comparative work – choosing a culture

Look at the suggestions for comparative work after the story 'The Two Grandmothers'.

10. Wider reading

● 'Joebell and America' was first published in an anthology of short stories by Earl Lovelace called *A Brief Conversation and other stories*. There are several other stories with male heroes in this collection: 'A Brief Conversation', 'The Fire Eater's Journey', 'The Coward', 'The Fire Eater's Return', 'Fleurs' and 'Shoemaker Arnold'.

● Lovelace's novel, *The Dragon Can't Dance*, has much of the same atmosphere and style as 'Joebell and America', and is peopled with a lively range of characters such as one finds in this story.

● Lawrence Scott's collection of stories, *Ballad for the New World and Other Stories* is also set in Trinidad. The stories deal with people's lives, emotions and confused sense of their own identities, from an adult who wants to take part in carnival to a young boy who struggles to understand the complicated relationships and racial divisions around him.

● James Baldwin has written about the experience of being a black American man, rather than a recent arrival to the United States. His short stories, in the collection *Going to Meet the Man* provide some alternative viewpoints, histories and contexts to those presented by Earl Lovelace.

● In *The Friends* Rosa Guy tells of a Jamaican girl's experiences when her family emigrate to New York.

● *A View from the Bridge* is a play by Arthur Miller about an Italian family recently arrived in the USA.

Kreativ Riting

'Today, we are going to do some writing,' says PK. 'Some *creative* writing. You do know what I mean by *creative,* Joe, don't you?'

This is what he says to me. So I says to him:

'Eh... Is that like when ye use they fancy letters an that?'

'No, Joe, it is not. Creative writing has nothing whatsoever to do with 'they fancy letters an that',' says PK.

So I made the face like Neanderthal Man and went:

'UHHH!'

We call him PK cause his name is Pitcairn and he is a nut. So anyway, he goes round and gives everybody a new jotter each.

'For God's sake now, try and use a bit of imagination!'

Then he stops at my desk and he looks at me like I am a puzzle he is trying to work out and he says:

'If you've got one, I mean. You have got an imagination Joe, haven't you?'

This is him slaggin me, ken?

So I says to him:

'Naw, sir, but I've got a video.'

That got a laugh, ken?

So then PK says:

'The only trouble with you Joe is, your head is too chock-a-block with those videos and those video nasties. Those video nasties are worse than anything for your brain, Joe.'

Then Lenny Turnbull, who sits behind me and who is a poser, says:

'What brain? Joe's no got a brain in there, sir, just a bitty fresh air between his lugs!'

That got a laugh, ken?

So I turns round in my seat and I give Lenny Turnbull a boot in the shins, then he karate-chops me in the neck, so I slap him across his pus for him.

PK goes spare, ken?

Except nobody takes any notice, so he keeps on shouting:

'That's *enough* of that! Come on now 4F, let's have a bit of order round here!'

So then I says:

'Sir, they video nasties is no as bad as glue is for your brains but, is it?'

That got a laugh, ken?

Then Lenny Turnbull (poser) says:

'Joe's got brain damage, sir, through sniffin too much glue!'

'Glue sniffing... solvent abuse... is no laughing matter. Now let's have a bit of *order round here*! Right, I'm going to get you all to do a piece of writing today. You've got a whole two periods to do it in, and what I'd like all of you to do is empty your mind. In your case, Joe, that shouldn't be too difficult.'

This is PK slaggin me again, ken?

So I says for a laugh ken:

'How no, sir? I thought you said my mind was chock-a-block with video nasties?'

Then PK says:

'That's right Joe, and what I want you to do is just empty all that stuff out of your mind, so that your mind is completely blank, so that you've got a blank page in your mind, just like the one in your jotter – understand?'

'But sir, this jotter's no blank – it's got lines in it!'

'Joe, your head probably has lines in it too, through watching all those video nasties.'

Everybody laughed at that, so I made the face like Neanderthal Man again and started hitting my skull with my fist and went:

'UHHH! UHHH!'

'Joe, I knew you'd hit the headlines one day,' says PK.

Nobody laughed at that, so PK says:

'You are a slow lot today, aren't you?'

So I did the face again and went:

'UHHH!'

'Right. As I was saying before I was so rudely interrupted, what I want you to do is empty out your mind. It's a bit like meditating.'

'What's meditatin? Is that like deep-sea divin an that?' says Podge Grogan, who sits beside me.

'Not quite.'

'Of course it's no! Deep-sea divin!' says Lenny Poser Turnbull.

'Well,' says Podge, 'it coulda been! That's what it sounds like, eh Joe? Deep-sea divin in the Mediterranean an that.'

'Aye, that's right enough. Deep-sea meditatin, Ah've heard o that!'

'Away ye go! Deep-sea meditatin! Yez are off yer heids, you two!' says Lenny.

'Meditating,' says PK, 'as far as I know, has nothing to do with deep-sea diving at all, although when you think about it, the two activities could be compared. You could say that deep-sea diving and meditating are... similar.'

So me and Podge turns round in our seats and looks at Lenny Turnbull.

'See?' says Podge. 'Deep-sea meditatin. Tellt ye.'

'They're no the same at aw,' says Lenny. 'Ah mean, ye dinnae need a harpoon tae meditate, eh no sir?'

'Ye dae in the Mediterranean,' says Podge.

'Aye,' I says, 'it's fulla sharks an that, course ye need a harpoon.'

'Aye,' says Lenny, 'but you're talkin aboot deep-sea divin, no meditatin!'

'Well Lenny,' says PK, 'maybe you could tell the class what meditating is.'

'Aw, it's what they Buddhist monks dae.'

'Yes, but how do they do it?'

'Aw, they sit wi their legs crossed an chant an aw that.'

'Naw they dinnae,' says Podge Grogan, 'cause Ah've seen them. They dance aboot an shake wee bells thegither an that an sing Harry Krishner, that's how they dae it!'

'That's different,' says Lenny, 'that's no them meditatin, eh no sir?'

'Well no, I don't think so. In any case, there are different ways of meditating, but basically you have to empty your mind. You'll find it's harder to do than you think. Your mind will keep thinking of things, all the little things that clutter our minds up every day.'

'How's that like deep-sea divin, sir?' says Lenny.

'Well, it's hard to explain Lenny, I just meant that when you meditate you sort of dive into your mind, you dive into the depths of your mind and that's what I want you to try to do today. If you're lucky, you might find something there you didn't know was there.'

'Dae we get tae use harpoons?' says Podge.

'No,' says PK. 'Pens.'

Everybody goes: 'AWWW!'

'Now listen,' says PK. 'It's quite simple really. All I really want you to do is write in your jotter whatever floats into your mind. I don't want you to think about it too much, just let it flow. OK?'

'OK, PK!'

'Anything at all. It doesn't have to be a story. It doesn't have to be a poem. It doesn't have to be anything. Just whatever comes into your heads when you've emptied out your minds. Just let your mind *open up*, let the words *flow* from your subconscious mind, through your pen into your jotter. It's called Automatic Writing, and you're lucky to get a teacher like me who lets you do something like Automatic Writing, especially first two periods on a Wednesday.'

This is still PK talkin, ken. Then he says:

'I don't even want you to worry about punctuation or grammar or anything like that, just let your imagination roam free – not that you worry about punctuation anyway, you lot.'

So I says for a laugh, ken:

'Sir, what's punk-tuition? Is that like *learnin* tae be a punk?'

Everybody groaned. PK rolls his eyes and says:

'Joe, will you just shut up please?'

So I says for a laugh, ken:

'Hear that? First he's tellin us tae open up and now he's tellin us tae *shut up!*'

That got a laugh, ken?

Lenny Turnbull (poser) says:

'But sir, what if nothin comes intae yer heid when ye're sittin there wi yer pen at the ready?'

'Anyway,' I says. '*How* can I write anyway, cause I've no got a pen?'

'Use yer harpoon!' says Lenny.

'You can borrow my pen,' says PK. 'But it's more than a pen you'll need to write, Joe, because to write you also need inspiration.'

'What's that, a new flavour o chewing gum, or what?' says Podge Grogan. So everybody starts laughin and PK goes spare again, ken. Then he brings this cassette out of his briefcase and he says:

'Right, I want you to listen to this piece of music I've got here, so that it might give you some inspiration to get you going. Just listen to the music, empty your mind, and write down whatever comes out of the music into your heads. OK?'

'OK, PK!'

'What is it, sir? Is it The Clash?'

'No, it is none of that Clash-trash. That Clash-trash is even worse for your brain than video nasties *or* glue, Joe.'

Everybody laughed, so I did the face.

'UHHH!'

'If the wind changes, your face might stay like that, Joe. Right, now stop wasting time. The music you are about to hear is not The Clash, but a great piece of classical music by Johann Sebastian Bach.'

'Who's she?' says Podge Grogan.

'*He*,' says PK, 'was a musical genius who wrote *real* music, the likes of which you lot have probably never heard before and probably won't know how to appreciate even when you do. Now I want you to be very quiet and listen very carefully to this wonderful classical piece of music and just *let go, let go*, and write absolutely anything the music makes you think and feel about. It's called "Air on a G string".'

'Hair on a g-string?' I says.

Everybody fell about, ken?

'Come on now 4F, let's have a bit of order round here!'

Then Lenny Turnbull says:

'But sir, can we write *absolutely* anything we want, even swearin an that?'

'Absolutely anything you want to,' says PK. 'Just listen to the music and *let go*. I promise no member of staff will see it except me. If you don't even want me to read it, I won't. The choice is yours. You can either read out what you've written to the class, or you can give it to me and I promise you it will be destroyed. OK?'

'OK, PK!'

Then Lenny Turnbull says:

'But sir, what about sex an that – can we put sex in it as well?'

'Hold on a minute,' says PK.

So I says for a laugh, ken:

'Hear that? First he tells us to *let go*, and now he's tellin us to *hold on*!'

That got a laugh, ken?

Then PK started clenching his fists so the knuckles went white, and he glared at me and his face went beetroot like he was ready to go completely raj.

'Look here you lot, we haven't got all day. You've wasted nearly a whole period already with your carry-on and I am sick to the back teeth of having to RAISE MY VOICE IN HERE TO MAKE MYSELF HEARD! Will you please sit *still*, keep your hands *on* the desk and YOU, Joe Murdoch, are asking for *trouble*! One more wise-crack out of you and you will be out that door and along that corridor to pay a visit to the *rector*! Do I make myself clear?'

I sort of make a long face.

'As I was saying, you may write anything you like, but I don't think this piece of music will make you think about sex, because it is not an obscene bit of music at all. In fact it is one of the most soothing pieces of music I know, so *shut up* and listen to it!'

So then PK gets the cassette machine out of the cupboard where it is kept locked up in case it walks and he plugs it in and he plays us the music. Everybody sits there and yawns.

Then Podge Grogan says:

'Sir, I've heard this before!'

'Aye, so've I!' everybody starts saying. Then Lenny Turnbull says:

'Aye! It's that tune on the advert for they Hamlet cigars!'

So then everybody starts smokin their pens like cigars and PK switches off the music.

'Put your pens *down*! Any more of this and I'm going to keep you in over the break! I am aware that this music has been used in an advertisement, but this is not the point of it at all. The point is, it was written centuries ago and has survived even until today, so *belt up and listen to it*!'

So we all sat there and listened to the music till it was finished, but nobody got any inspiration out of it at all. So then PK says:

'If anybody is stuck, you could always write something about yourself. Describe yourself as you think other people might see you. "Myself As Others See Me." Now I've got a stack of prelims to mark, so I want you to keep quiet for the rest of the time and get on with it.

So that's what I did, and here it is. This is my kreativ, autematick, deep-sea-meditatin riting:

MY OWN SELF AS OTHERS MITE SEE ME

MY NAME IS JOE MURDOCH AND I AM SHEER MENTAL SO WATCH OUT I HAVE GOT A GREEN MOHAWK IT HAS GOT SKARLIT SPIKES ON MY FOUR HEAD I HAVE GOT A SKUL AND KROSS-BONES ON MY BLACK LETHER JAKET I HAVE GOT AT LEAST 200 KROME STUDS NOT COUNTIN THE STUDS ON MY LETHER BELT AND MY DOG KOLLAR ON MY NECK I HAVE GOT A TATOO IT SAYS KUT ALONG THE DOTTED LINE ON MY BACK I HAVE GOT NO FUTURE ON MY BOOTS I

HAVE GOT NO HOPE IN MY POCKET I HAVE GOT NO MONEY BUT MY MUM LOVES ME AND I LOVE HER BACK AND MY DAD STOLE THE LED OF THE DALKEITH EPISCAPALIEN CHURCH ROOF AND I GAVE HIM A HAND AND WE DIDNET GET CAUGHT HA HA I AM A WARRIER AND I AM SHEER FUCKEN MENTAL SO WATCH OUT O.K.

THE END

And now I will take out my kreativ riting to PK and tell him I don't want to read it out to the class and I don't want him to read it either. I will tell him I want it to be *destroyed*.

That should get a laugh, ken?

Brian McCabe

Working on Kreativ Riting

1. Classroom talk
● The phrase printed below is taken from a short story based in a classroom. Use it as the start of a short role-play of a typical classroom conversation between a teacher and some pupils.
'That's enough of that! Come on now 4F, let's have a bit of order round here!'

2. Joe Murdoch
● Talk about these issues:

– what is his attitude to the teacher and to the lesson?
– how does the reader get to know him/through whose eyes do we see him?
– why do you think he finally writes what he does as his piece of creative writing?
– why do you think he says that he will ask the teacher to destroy it?
– do you think the writer sees events through Joe's eyes or through the teacher's eyes?
– is Joe the hero of the story?

3. What's the point of the story
● What do you think the writer is trying to do with this simple situation of a teacher asking a class to write spontaneously? Look at the list below and decide which you think are most true.

– the writer is trying to be funny and entertaining
– there are some serious issues being tackled in the story
– the writer is trying to recreate a typical classroom scene
– the teacher's failures are the focus of the story
– the story is about education and working class children

4. The opening of a TV drama
Although this story has a very visual and authentic feel to it, interestingly there is almost no visual description – its realism comes entirely from the dialogue and the way language is used.
● Imagine the story is to be adapted for a TV screenplay, and you have been asked to construct a storyboard or shooting script for the opening few moments, say up to 'You are a slow lot today aren't you?' on page 110. Before you get down to detailed planning, think about the following questions:

– Who is the audience for a story like this and what will they need to know or see to establish their expectations for the story? What kind of school is this, and what details will you need to construct atmosphere?
– How will you establish a sense of place? Would you include extra shots not in the actual story e.g. the outside of the school building, shots of the corridors, staffroom, playground, PK arriving in the classroom, or shots of the students preparing for the lesson before it starts?
– How might you use music and sound effects to set up atmosphere?
– What will the characters look like visually? How do they dress, sit, interact with each other?
– How might the classroom be laid out?

• Once you've decided on these issues, concentrate on the following:

– How will you adapt the script for your audience? Will you keep the Scottish dialect words and phrases, and the swear words?
– Will you include all the dialogue, or make cuts?
– How will you use camera angles and movement, transition from one shot to the next, and the use of close-up shots to demonstrate the interaction between students and teacher?

• Now try breaking the story down into a sequence of separate shots, and sketch them out as a storyboard. Beside each frame, indicate the action, dialogue and other sound-track accompanying the shot, together with instructions for the camera operator – e.g. high-angle wide-angle shot of classroom, zooming in from the back of the room to close-up on PK.
• If you have the facilities, you could try actually shooting your final storyboard on video to see how successfully your planning has represented your reading of the opening.

5. Classroom stories
• Write your own story, or short playscript, about a scene in a classroom. You could use something that really happened in your class and try re-creating it as a story. Use real bits of classroom dialogue from your own experience of school to make it sound authentic.

6. Comparative work – young people
• Look at the other short stories in this collection about young people: 'Dear George', 'The Potato Gatherers', 'A Basket Full of Wallpaper', 'My Son the Fanatic' and 'The Two Grandmothers'.
• Choose three characters from different stories and compare them, exploring what kind of characters they are, how the writers have created them and presented them to the reader. Think about how each writer has represented adolescence and what you think of the way in which it has been portrayed. How interesting and realistic is the portrayal? What are the similarities and differences in approach between the writers?

7. Wider reading

● *Gregory's Girl*, a filmscript by Bill Forsyth, has a school setting and like 'Kreativ Riting', uses humour to portray its teenage characters. The film, which was also directed by Bill Forsyth, is available on video.

● *Our Day Out*, by Willy Russell, was originally screened as a TV play. It is a humorous presentation of school children and their teachers on a school outing.

● Frank O'Connor's 'The Idealist', in the English & Media Centre publication *School*, is a powerful story about a boy's experience of school and attitudes to it.

● Trevor Millum's collection, *Warning – Too Much Schooling Can Damage Your Health*, contains many witty poems about school life.

● *Jane Eyre* [GCSE], by Charlotte Bronte, contains scenes from the heroine's schooldays in a bleak and often cruel girls' boarding school.

● *Hard Times* [GCSE], by Charles Dickens also contains several school scenes where the atmosphere and activities are very different from those in 'Kreativ Writing'.

● Schools have been the focus of a number of TV dramas. David Leland wrote four TV dramas in the early 1980s, all of which dealt with aspects of school and youth culture. *Birth of a Nation, Flying into the Wind, Rhino* and *Made in Britain* are powerful plays about how education and society fail young people. *Hearts and Minds*, written by the Scottish writer Jimmy McGovern, was a recent TV drama series about the harsh realities of an inner city comprehensive school. *Grange Hill* is a children's soap about life in a school. You could look at different ways in which school is represented in some of these dramas.

A Basket Full of Wallpaper

Some people said that he'd been a chicken-sexer during the forties, a pale and narrow man who had spent his days interned in a camp for the Japanese near the mountains of Idaho. Endless months spent determining whether chickens were male or female. He had come to Ireland to forget it all. At other times, the older men, elbows on the bar counter, invented heinous crimes for him. In Japan, they said, he had attached electrical cords to the testicles of airmen, ritually sliced prisoners with swords, operated slow drip torture on young Marines. They said he had that sort of face. Dark eyes falling down into sunken cheeks, a full mouth without any colour, a tiny scar over his right eye. Even the women created a fantastic history for him. He was the fourth son of an emperor, or a poet, or a general, carrying the baggage of unrequited love. To us boys at school he was a kamikaze pilot who had gotten cold feet, barrelling out in a parachute and somehow drifting to our town, carried by some ferocious, magical wave.

On the beach he walked with his head slung low to the ground, stooping to collect stones. We would sometimes hide in the dunes, parting the long grass to watch him, his trouser pockets filling up with stones. He had a long rambling stride, sometimes walking for hours along the coast, the gulls hurling themselves up from the strand, small fishing boats bobbing on the sea. When I was twelve years old I saw him leap along the beach while a porpoise surfaced and resurfaced in the water, fifty yards away. Once Paul Ryan wrapped a note around a brick and flung it through the window of his cottage, one of a row of fifteen small houses in the centre of our village. *Nip go home* said the note. The following day we noticed that the window had been covered with wallpaper and Paul Ryan went home from school with blood caked under his nose because we could no longer see through Osobe's front window.

Osobe had come to Ireland before I was born, some time in the fifties. He was a curious sight in any Irish town, his black hair sticking out like conifer needles, his eyes shaded by the brim of his brown hat. He had bought the cottage, a delapidated two-room affair, from an out-of-town landlord who thought that Osobe might just stay for a month or two. But, according to my father, a huge lorry carrying reams and reams of wallpaper pulled up to the cottage during the first summer of his visit. Osobe and two hefty Dubliners lifted all the paper into the house and later he hung a sign on his front window: 'Wallpaper for Sale – Ask Inside'. There were mutterings about how the paper had been stolen, how it had been imported from Japan at a ridiculous price, undercutting the Irish wholesalers. Nobody bought any for a month until my Aunt Moira, who was infamous for having gotten drunk with Brendan Behan in a Republican pub in Dublin, knocked on his door and ordered a floral pattern with a touch of pink for her living room.

Osobe rode his black bicycle along by the river out to her house. Rolls of paper, cans of glue, knives and brushes were stuffed into the basket. My Aunt said he did a wonderful job, although people muttered about her outside mass on Sunday mornings. 'He was as quiet then as he is now,' she told me. 'No more noise out of him than a dormouse and we should leave it that way. He's a good man who never done anyone a whit of harm.' She laughed at the rumours that hung around him.

By the time I was born he was a fixture around town, no stranger than the newspaper editor whose handkerchiefs drooped from his trouser pockets, the shopkeeper who stole all the footballs that landed in her back garden, the soldier who had lost his right hand while fighting for Franco. People nodded to him on the streets and, in Gaffney's pub, he was left alone over his morning pint of Guinness. He had a brisk trade going with the wallpaper and occasionally when Kieran O'Malley, the local handyman, was sick, he was called out to unblock a toilet or fix a crooked door. There was talk that he was seeing a young girl from Galway, a madwoman who walked around with three sleeves sewn on her dresses. But that had about as much truth as all the other rumours – or less in fact, since he was never seen to leave town, not even on his bicycle.

He spoke English only haltingly and in the shops he would whisper for a packet of cigarettes or a jar of jam. On Sundays he never wore his brown hat. Girls giggled when he passed them in the street, a red Japanese sun umbrella held above his head.

I was sixteen years old when he hung a sign on his front door, looking for help with a wallpaper job. It was a hot summer, the ground was bone dry, and there were no seasonal jobs in the fields. My father would moan at the dinner table about the huge toll that emigration was having on his undertaking business. 'Everyone's gone somewhere else to die,' he'd say. 'Even that bloody Mrs Hynes is hanging on for dear life.' One evening my mother came and sat by my bed, mashing her fingers together nervously. She muttered under her breath that I should get some work with the Japanese man, that I was old enough now to put some bread on the table. I had noticed that, in the bread that she baked at home, there were no currants anymore.

The following morning, in a blue wool jumper and old working trousers, I sidled down to his house and knocked on his door.

The cottage was filled with rolls of wallpaper. They were stacked on top of each other all around the room, crowding in towards the small table and two wooden chairs. Most of it was muted in colour, but together they made a strange collage, flowers and vines and odd shapes all meshed together. The walls themselves had been papered with dozens of different types and the smell of paste was heavy in the house. On the ground sat rows and rows of small paper dolls, the faces painted almost comically. An old philosopher, a young girl, a wizened woman, a soldier. A row of Japanese books lay in one corner. On top of them, a pan of sliced bread. Cigarette packages littered the floor.

There was a collection of beach stones on the mantlepiece. I noticed lots of change and a few pound notes scattered around the cottage and a twenty pound note stuffed under a lamp. A kettle whistled on the stove and he filled up two china cups with tea.

'Welcome,' he said. The saucer rattled in my fingers. 'There is big job in house. You will help me?'

I nodded and sipped at the tea, which tasted peculiarly bitter. His hands were long and spindly. I noticed the liver spots gathering up from his wrists. A grey shirt slouched on his thin shoulders.

'You will go home and get bicycle, in this afternoon we start. Very good?'

We rode out together to the old Gorman house which had lain empty for three years. Osobe whistled as we pedalled and people stared at us from their cars and houses. Five rolls of pale green wallpaper were balanced in his front basket and I carried two cans of paste in my right hand, steering the bicycle with the other. I saw Paul Ryan hanging out by the school, smoking a long cigar. 'Ya get slanty eyes from wanking too much, Donnelly,' he shouted, and I tucked my head down towards the handlebars.

The Gorman House had been bought by an American millionaire just three months before. There were schoolboy rumours that the American drove a huge Cadillac and had five blonde daughters who would be fond of the local disco and, on excellent authority, were known to romp behind haystacks. But there was nobody there when we arrived on our bicycles. Osobe produced a set of keys from his overalls and walked slowly through the house, pointing at the walls, smotes of dust kicking up from behind him. We made five trips on the bikes that day, carrying reams of wallpaper and paste each time. At the end of the day, after I had carried a ladder over my shoulder from his house, he produced a brand new ten pound note and offered it to me.

'Tomorrow we start,' he said, and then he bowed slightly.

'You are fast on bicycle,' he said.

I went outside. The sun was slouching over the town. I heard Osobe humming in the background as I leaped on my bike and rode towards home, the money stuffed down deep in my pocket.

*   *   *

That summer I read books in my bedroom and I wanted Osobe to tell me a fabulous story about his past. I suppose I wanted to own something of him, to make his history belong to me.

It would have something to do with Hiroshima, I had decided, with the children of the pikadon, the flash boom. There would be charred telegraph poles and tree trunks, a wasteland of concrete, a single remaining shell of a building. People with melted faces would run wildly through the streets. Bloated corpses would float down the Ota River. The slates on the roofs of houses would bubble. He would spit on the American and British soldiers as they sat under burnt cherry blossom trees, working the chewing gum over in their mouths. Perhaps, in his story, he would reach out for the festered face of a young girl. Or massage the burnt scalp of a boy. A woman friend of his would see her reflection in a bowl of soup and howl. Maybe he would run off towards the hills and never stop. Or perhaps he would simply just walk away, down narrow roads, in wooden sandals, a begging bowl in his hands. It would be a peculiar Buddhist hell, that story of his, and a B-29 would drone in constantly from the clouds.

But Osobe stayed silent almost the whole time as he stood in that big old house and rolled paste on the walls in long smooth motions, humming gently as the house began to take on colour. 'Sean,' he would say to me in comically broken English, with his face cocked into a smile, 'some day you will be great wallpaper man. You must think how important this job. We make people happy or sad if we do bad job.'

He would buy big bottles of Club Orange and packets of Goldgrain biscuits, and spread them out on the ground during lunch time. He brought a radio one morning and his old body swayed with laughter as he tuned in to a pop station from Dublin. Once, for a joke, he swiped a ladder away from me and left me hanging from a door ledge. He was deft with a knife, slicing the wallpaper in one smooth motion. At the end of the day he would sit and smoke two cigarettes, allowing me a puff at the end of each. Then he would go back into the house and sit, lotus-legged, in front of the most newly decorated wall and nod, smiling gently, rocking back and forth.

'What is Japan like?' I asked him one evening as we were cycling home, my palms sweaty.

'Like everywhere else. Not as beautiful like this,' he said, sweeping his arms around the fields and hills.

'Why did you come here?'

'So long ago.' He pointed at his nose. 'Don't remember. Sorry.'

'Were you in the war?'

'You ask lots of questions.'

'Somebody told me you were in Hiroshima.'

He laughed uproariously, slapping his thighs. 'These questions,' he said. 'I have no answer.' He rode silently for a while. 'Hiroshima was sad place. Japanese don't talk about.'

'Were you in Hiroshima?' I asked again.

'No, no,' he said. 'No, no.'

'Do you hate Americans?'

'Why?'

'Because... '

'You are very young. You shouldn't think these things. You should think of making good job with wallpaper. That is important.'

We rode out to the house at eight every morning. The lawn was dry and cracked. The third floor windows were black with soot. When the radio played it could be heard all over the house. Osobe worked with tremendous energy. In the hot afternoons I could see his sinewy arms under the sleeves of his rolled-up shirts. Once, when the radio told us of an earthquake in Japan, he blanched and said that the country was suffering from too much pain.

In the evenings I started going down to the bridge with my friends to drink flagons of cider with the money I held back from my parents. I began to buy my own cigarettes. I read books about World War Two and created fabulous lies about how he had been in that southern Japanese city when the bomb had been dropped, how his family had been left as shadows on the Town Hall walls, all of them vapourised, disappeared. He had been ten miles from the epicentre of the blast, I said, in the shadow of a building, wearing billowy orange carpenter pants and a large straw hat. He was flung to the ground, and when he awoke the city was howling all around him. He had never found his family. They were scattered around the centre, dark patches of people left on broken concrete. He had reeled away from the pain of it all, travelling the world, ending up eventually in the West of Ireland. My friends whistled through their teeth. Under the bridge they pushed the bottle towards me.

Occasionally my mother and father asked me about Osobe, muted questions, probings, which they slid in at dinner time after I had handed over most of my wages.

'He's a strange one, that one,' said my father.

'Hiding something, I'd guess,' my mother would respond, the fork clanging against her teeth.

'Bit of a mad fellow, isn't he, Sean?'

'Ah, he's not too bad,' I said.

'People say he lived in Brazil for a while.'

'God knows, he could have,' said my mother.

'He doesn't tell me anything,' I said.

For all I really knew, he had just wandered to our town, for no good or sufficient reason, and decided to stay. I had an uncle in Ghana, an older brother in Nebraska, a distant cousin who worked as a well-digger near Melbourne, none of which struck me as peculiar. Osobe was probably just one of their breed, a wanderer, a misfit, although I didn't want him to be.

We worked through that hot summer together, finished the Gorman house and started on a few others. I grew to enjoy clambering along the roads on our bicycles in the morning, slapping paste on the walls, inventing tales about him for my friends down under the bridge. Some of my friends were working in the chipper, others were bringing in the tired hay, and a couple of them were selling golf balls down at the club. Every evening I continued with Osobe stories for them, their faces lit up by a small fire we kept going. We all nodded and slurped at the bottles, fascinated by the horror and brilliance of it all. Fireballs had raged throughout the city as he fled, I told them. People ran with sacks of rice in their melted hands. A Shinto monk said prayers over the dead. Strange weeds grew in clumps where the plum trees once flowered and Osobe wandered away from the city, half-naked, his throat and eyes burning.

$$* \quad * \quad *$$

Osobe opened the door to me one morning towards the end of summer. 'All the jobs almost done,' he said. 'We celebrate with cup of tea.'

He guided me gently by the arm to the chair in the middle of the room. Looking around I noticed that he had been wallpapering again. He had papered over the paper. But there were no bubbles, no stray ends, no spilt paste around the edges. I imagined him staying up late at night, humming as he watched the patterns close in on him. The rest of the cottage was a riot of odds and ends – dishes and teacups, an oriental fan, wrapped slices of cheese, a fouton rolled in the corner. There was a twenty pound note sitting on the small gas heater near the table. Another ten pound note lay on the floor, near the table. His brown hat was hung up over the door. There were paintbrushes everywhere.

'You did good job,' he said. 'Will you go soon school?'

'In a few weeks.'

'Will you one day paper? Again. If I find you job ?' he said.

Before I could answer he had sprung to his heels to open the front door for a marmalade-coloured cat, which had been scratching at the door. It was a stray. We often saw it slinking around the back of the chipper, waiting for some scraps. John Brogan once tried to catch it with a giant net, but couldn't. It scurried away from everyone. Osobe leaned down on his hunkers and, swooping his arms as if he was going to maul it, he got the cat to come closer. It was almost a windmill motion, smoothly through the air, his thin arms making arcs. The cat stared. Then, with a violent quickness, Osobe scooped it up, turned it on its back, pinned it down with one hand and roughly stroked his other hand along it. The cat leaned its head back and purred. Osobe laughed.

For a moment I felt a vicious hatred for him and his quiet ways, his mundane stroll through the summer, his ordinariness, the banality of everything he had become for me. He should have been a hero, or a seer. He should have told me some incredible story that I could carry with me forever. After all, he had been the one who had run along the beach parallel to a porpoise, who filled his pockets full of pebbles, who could lift the stray orange cat in his fingers.

I looked around the room for a moment while he hunched down with the cat, his back to me. I was hoping to find something, a diary, a picture, a drawing, a badge, anything that would tell me a little more about him. Looking over my shoulder I reached across to the gas heater, picked up the twenty pound note and stuffed it in my sock, then pulled my trousers down over it. I sat at the wooden table, my hands shaking. After a while Osobe turned and came over towards me with the cat in his hands, stroking it with the same harsh motion as before. With his right hand he reached into his overalls and gave me a hundred pounds in ten new notes. 'For you school.' I could feel the other twenty pound note riding up in my sock and as I backed out the door a sick feeling rose in my stomach.

'You did very good job,' he said. 'Come back for visit.'

It was only afterwards that I realised I never got the cup of tea he offered.

That night, full of cider, I stumbled away from the bridge and walked down along the row of houses where Osobe lived. I climbed around the back of the house, through the hedge, along by some flowerpots, rattling an old wheelbarrow as I moved up to the window. He was there, slapping paste on the wall in gentle arcs. I counted five separate sheets and the wall must have come a good quarter of an inch closer to him. I wanted him to be sloppy this time, not to smooth the sheets out, to wield the knife in a slipshod way, but he did the job as always, precise and fluid. The whole time he was humming and I stood, drunk, rattling the change from the twenty pound note in the bottom of my pockets.

*　　*　　*

Years later when I was acquiring an English accent in the East End of London, I got a letter from my father. Business was still slow and a new wave of emigration had left its famous scars. Old Mrs Hynes still hadn't kicked the bucket. Five of the new council houses were empty now and even the Gorman House had been sold once more. The American in his Cadillac had never arrived with his five blonde daughters. The hurling team had lost all its matches again this year. There was a bumper crop of hay.

On the last page of the letter he told me that Osobe had died. The body was not discovered for three days, until my old Aunt Moira called around with a basket of fruit for him. When my father went into the house he said the stench was so bad that he almost vomited. Children gathered at the front door with their hands held to their noses. But there was a whipround made in Gaffney's pub that extended out to the streets. People threw generous amounts of money in a big brown hat that the owner of the chipper carried from door to door. My aunt chose him a fine coffin, although someone said that he might have been offended by it, that he should have been sent back to Japan to be cremated. She scoffed at the suggestion and made a bouquet of flowers for him.

There was a party held the night of the funeral and rumours were flung around according to the depths of the whiskey bottle – but more or less everyone was sure now that he had been a victim of Hiroshima. All the young boys who had worked for him in the summer months had heard vivid details of that frightening August morning. He had fled from the city in a pair of wooden sandals. All his family had been killed. They had been vapourised. He was a man in flight. By the late, sober hours of the morning, my father added, the talk was that Osobe was a decent sort, no matter what his history was. Over the years he had employed many young men to work with him, treated them fairly, paid them handsomely and confided in them about his life. They laughed at how strange his accent had become at the end of it all – when he went to the shop to buy cigarettes he would lean over the counter and whisper for *pack of fags prease.* The sight of him carrying that big ladder on his bicycle would be sorely missed around town.

But the strangest thing of all, my father said, was that when he had gone into the house to recover the body the room had seemed very small to him. It was customary to burn the bedsheets and scrape the paper from the walls when someone had been dead that long. But he took a knife to the paper and discovered it was a couple of feet thick, though it didn't seem so at first glance. Layers and layers of wallpaper. It looked as if Osobe had been gathering the walls into himself, probably some sort of psychological effect brought on by the bomb. Because the wallpaper had been so dense my father and some members of the town council simply had to knock the house down, burying everything that Osobe owned in the rubble. There had been no clues in the house, no letters, no medical papers, nothing to indicate that he had come from that most horrific of our century's moments.

It was a pathetic gesture, but I rode my bicycle around London that night. I ploughed along to no particular place, furious in the pedals. Blood thumped in me. Sweat leaped from my brow. The chain squeaked. A road in Ireland rose up – a road of grass grown ochre in the summer heat, a very thin figure in a brown hat along the river, a cat the colour of the going sun, a certain wall brought forward in slow movements, a road that wound forever through dry fields towards a grey beach, a road long gone, a road flung out elsewhere, a road that was still within me somewhere. I found myself down by the Thames in the early morning – it was rolling along in a desultory grey. I dropped a single twenty pound note into the water and watched it as it spun away very slowly, very deliberately, with the current, down towards some final sea, to fête the dead, their death, and their dying too.

Colum McCann

Working on A Basket Full of Wallpaper

1. Local characters

Most people have memories from childhood of some local character, a misfit or outsider who was a mystery to them, who seemed particularly interesting or frightening or odd.

● Write a paragraph about a person like that who you remember, then share anecdotes with someone else in your class. Talk about how differently you see that person now that you are older.

During reading

2. A close reading of the first paragraph

● Try answering these questions by looking closely at the text:

– who's it about?
– what do we know about him?
– who's talking?
– when is it happening?

● Look closely at the last sentence of the paragraph and sum up what view of Osobe the boys have.

3. Stop reading at the break in the story at the end of page 120

● Sum up what the boy thought about Osobe before he went to work for him.
● Read the next paragraph closely and talk about it. In what ways have the boy's views changed?

'That summer I read books in my bedroom and I wanted Osobe to tell me a fabulous story about his past. I suppose I wanted to own something of him, to make his history belong to me.'

● Read the paragraph that follows. Talk about what fantasies the boy has about Osobe. What would he like his history to be?

4. Stop reading at the break on page 124

● Why is this an important incident in the story? What do you feel about:

– the boy's behaviour?
– Osobe's behaviour and what it tells you about him?
– the boy's feelings afterwards?

5. The narrator's attitude to Osobe

● Chart the narrator's knowledge of Osobe and his changing attitudes towards him in the story. Each time you record his feelings look for one short quote as evidence of this.

	What he knows	What he feels	What he tells other people about Osobe
Before he was born			
By the time of his birth			
At sixteen			
The beginning of the summer			
When he started working for him			
During that summer			
The end of the summer			
Years later, in London			

● Look closely at your chart and try to summarise the main changes in the narrator's attitudes and feelings in the course of the story.
● In small groups, talk about what you think the story is about.

6. The community's view of Osobe

● In pairs, role-play one of these conversations about Osobe between different members of the community:

– Paul Ryan talking to one of the other local boys, having heard that the narrator has started working for Osobe
– the narrator's father talking to another man in the local bar
– Aunt Moira talking to one of the local women who is suspicious of Osobe
– two children standing outside Osobe's house after his body has been found
– two townspeople at the funeral, who have had a bit too much to drink

Before you start, look back to the text to find any relevant material that relates to your characters, or gives you clues as to what they might be thinking or feeling.
● Perform your role-plays for each other, without saying who you are. See if other people in the class can guess your roles.

7. Who is Osobe?

The narrator and the community are intrigued by Osobe and want to know more about him.

● Look through this list of possible facts about Osobe and sort them into two lists: what people think about him, and what is definitely true about him. In some cases you might have quite a long discussion to try to come to an agreement.

– a kamikaze pilot
– a victim of Hiroshima
– his family all perished in Hiroshima
– a Japanese internee in America
– a Japanese soldier who tortured American prisoners of war
– a misfit
– a good man
– an odd character
– a violent man
– a private, reserved person
– a man with a painful past
– a generous-spirited man
– someone with a guilty secret
– someone who is at peace with himself

● Make a third list of all of the statements that might be considered to be stereotypes of Japanese people. Which of these do you think are true of Osobe?

8. The wallpaper

Osobe's job as a wallpaperer could just be an ordinary job, but in the story it takes on more importance.

● Talk about what is unusual about Osobe and the wallpapering.

Knowing what you do about him as a character, what might his wallpapering say about his personality and about his state of mind? Could it be a metaphor for anything about him?

9. The ending

● Look closely at the last paragraph of the story. Read it aloud to hear the narrator's voice. What kind of tone is it written in? What does it suggest about the feelings and ideas behind the story?

● The last paragraph contains many references to things that have been important in the rest of the story. List all of the objects or places that come into the boy's mind and talk about why they are important enough to include in the ending.

10. Comparative work – isolated individuals

Look at the suggestions for comparative work after the short story 'American Dreams.'

11. Comparative work – young people

Look at the suggestions for comparative work after the story 'Kreativ Riting'.

12. Wider reading

● Colum McCann's collection, *Fishing the Sloe-Black River* contains other powerful and often unusual stories, set in Ireland and America.

● *Silas Marner* GCSE by George Eliot is a short nineteenth century novel, telling the story of a lonely man, an outsider in his community, who is obsessed with money. A surprise event suddenly changes his attitudes and those of the people around him.

● *Great Expectations* GCSE by Charles Dickens involves the relationship of a boy with an outcast from society, and how this relationship affects his life in dramatic ways.

● *The Yellow Wallpaper* by Charlotte Perkins Gilman explores an unhappy woman's state of mind, using similar metaphors to 'A Basket Full of Wallpaper'. It is anthologised in *The New Windmill Book of Nineteenth Century Short Stories* GCSE .

The Two Grandmothers

I

Mummy, you know what? Grandma Del has baby chickens. Yellow and white ones. She makes me hold them. And I help her gather eggs but I don't like to go out the back alone because the turkey gobbler goes gobble! gobble! gobble! after my legs, he scares me and Mr SonSon next door has baby pigs I don't like the mother pig though. Grandma lives in this pretty little house with white lace curtains at all the windows, Mummy you must come with me and Daddy next time and you can peek through the louvres Grandma calls them jalousies isn't that funny and you can see the people passing by. But they can't see you. Mummy why can't we have lace curtains like Grandma Del so we can peek though nobody ever goes by our house except the gardeners and the maids and people begging and Rastas selling brooms. Many many people go by Grandma Del's house and they all call out to her and Grandma Del knows everyone. My special friend is Miss Princess the postmistress who plays the organ in church she wears tight shiny dresses and her hair piled *so* on her head and she walks *very slow* and everybody says she is sweet on Mr Blake who is the new teacher and he takes the service in church when Parson doesn't come and Miss Princess gets so nervous she mixes up all the hymns. Mr Mack came to fix Grandma's roof and Grandma said 'poorman poorman' all the time. Mr Mack's daughters Eulalie and Ermandine are big girls at high school in town though Eulalie fell and they don't know what is to be done. Mummy, why are they so worried that Eulalie fell? She didn't break her leg or anything like that for she is walking up and down past the house all day long and looks perfectly fine to me.

Mummy, I really like Grandma Del's house it's nice and cosy and dark and cool inside with these big lovely oval picture frames of her family and Daddy as

130

a baby and Daddy as a little boy and Daddy on the high school football team, they won Manning Cup that year Grandma says did you know that Mummy? And Daddy at University and a wedding picture of Daddy and you and me as a baby and all the pictures you send Grandma every year but those are the small pictures on the side table with the lovely white lace tablecloth in the picture frame on the wall is Great-grandpapa Del with a long beard and whiskers he makes me giggle and he is sitting down in a chair and Great-grandmama is standing behind him and then there is a picture of Grandma herself as a young lady with her hair piled high like Miss Princess and her legs crossed at the ankles she looks so lovely. But you know what, Mummy, I didn't see a picture of Daddy's father and when I asked Grandma she got mad and shooed me away. She gets even madder when I asked her to show me her wedding picture. I only want to see it.

Mummy do you know that Grandma sends me to Sunday School? And then we stay over for big church and then I walk home with her and all the people it's so nice and only Parson comes to church in a car. Mummy did you go to Sunday School? I go with Joycie a big girl next door and Grandma made me three dresses to wear. She says she cannot imagine how a girl-child (that's me) can leave her home with nothing but blue-jeans and T-shirts and shorts and not a single church dress. She has this funny sewing machine, not like Aunt Thelma's, she has to use her feet to make it go just like the organ in church Miss Princess pumps away with her feet to make it give out this lovely sound she works so hard you should see her and the first time I went to Grandma's church I was so scared of the bats! The church is full of bats but usually they stay high up in the roof but as soon as the organ starts playing on Sunday the bats start swooping lower and lower and one swooped so low I nearly died of fright and clutched Grandma Del so tight my hat flew off.

Did I tell you Grandma made me a hat to go to church with her own two hands? She pulled apart one of her old straw hats, leghorn she said, and made me a little hat that fits just so on my head with a bunch of tiny pink flowers. Grandma didn't send it with me though or my Sunday dresses she says she will keep them till I return for she knows that I am growing heathenish in town. When Grandma dresses me up for church I feel so beautiful in my dresses she made with lace and bows and little tucks so beautiful and my hat, I feel so special that my own Grandma made these for me with her own two hands and didn't buy them in a store. Grandma loves to comb my hair she says it's so long and thick and she rubs it with castor oil every night. I hate the smell of castor oil but she says it's the best thing for hair to make it thick and soft and after a time I even like the smell. Grandma Del says my skin is beautiful like honey and all in all I am a fine brown lady and must make sure to grow as beautiful inside as I am outside but Mummy how do I go about doing that?

Nights at Grandma's are very funny. Mummy can you imagine there's no TV? And it's very, very dark. No street lights or any lights and we go to bed so early and every night Grandma lights the oil lamps and then we blow them out when we are going to bed, you have to take a deep breath and every morning Grandma checks the oil in the lamps and cleans the shades. They have 'Home

Sweet Home' written all around them. So beautiful. She cleans the shades with newspapers. She says when I come next year I'll be old enough to clean the shades all by myself. Grandma knows such lovely stories; she tells me stories every night not stories from a book you know, Mummy, the way you read to me, but stories straight from her head. Really! I am going to learn stories from Grandma so when I am a grown lady I will remember all these stories to tell my children. Mummy, do you think I will?

II

Mummy you know Grandma Elaine is so funny she says I'm not to call her Grandma any more, I'm to call her Towser like everybody else for I'm growing so fast nobody would believe that she could have such a big young lady for a granddaughter. I think it's funny I'm practising calling her Towser though she is still my grandmother. I say, 'Grandmother, I mean Towser', Grandma Del introduces me to everyone as her Granddaughter she calls me her 'little gran' and Grandma Elaine says, 'Darling, the way your Grandmother Del looks and conducts herself she couldn't be anything but a Grandmother and honey she and I are of entirely different generations.'

Grandma Elaine says such funny things sometimes. Like she was dressing to go out last night and she was putting on make-up and I said 'Grandma' – she was still Grandma then – I said, 'Grandma, you shouldn't paint your face like that you know, it is written in the Bible that it's a sin. Grandma Del says so and I will never paint my face.' And she said, 'Darling, with all due respect to your paternal Grandmother she's a lovely lady or was when I met her the one and only time at the wedding, and she has done one absolutely fantastic thing in her life which is to produce one son, your esteemed father, one hunk of a guy, but honey, other than that your Grandmother Del is a country bumpkin of the deepest waters and don't quote her goddamn sayings to me.' Mummy, you know Grandma Elaine *swears* like that all the time? I said 'Grandma you mustn't swear and take the name of the Lord in vain.' And she said, 'Honeychile with all due respect to the grey hairs of your old grandmother and the first-class brainwashing your daddy is allowing her to give you, I wish my granddaughter would get off my back and leave me to go to Hell in peace.' Can you imagine she said that?

She's really mad that you allow me to spend time with Grandma Del. She says, 'Honey, I really don't know what your mother thinks she is doing making you spend so much time down there in the deepest darkest country. I really must take you in hand. It's embarrassing to hear some of the things you come out with sometimes. Your mother would be better advised to send you to Charm School next summer you are never too young to start. Melody-Ann next door went last year and it's done wonders for her, turned her from a tomboy into a real little lady.' (Though Mummy, I really can't stand Melody-Ann any more, you know) 'And your mother had better start to do something about your hair from now it's almost as tough as your father's and I warned your mother about it from the very start I said "Honey, love's alright but what about the children's hair?" If you were my child I would cut it right off to get some of the kinks out.' Mummy, you won't cut off my hair, will you? Daddy and Grandma Del like it just the way it is and what does Grandma Elaine mean when she says my hair is tough, Mummy?

Anyway, Mummy, can I tell you a secret? Gran, I mean Towser, told me and says it's a secret but I guess since you are her daughter she won't mind if I tell you. Do you know that Towser has a new boyfriend? He came to pick her up on Saturday night, remember I told you Joyce was staying up with me and we watched TV together while Towser went out? That's the time she was painting her face and she put on her fabulous silver evening dress, you know the strapless one and her diamonds with it, the ones her husband after Grandpapa gave her, and I was so proud she was my grandmama she looked wonderful like a million dollars and when I told her so she let me spray some of her perfume on myself before Mr Kincaid came. He is a tall white man and he kissed Towser's hand and then he kissed my hand and he had a drink with Towser and was very nice and they drove off in this big white car like what Uncle Frank drives Mummy, a Benz, and Towser was looking so pleased the whole time and before Mr Kincaid came she whispered and said her new boyfriend was coming to take her to dinner and he was so nice and handsome and rich. Towser was looking as pleased as Eulalie did when the mail van driver was touching her when they thought nobody was looking but I was peeking through the louvres at Grandma Del's and I saw them.

But Mummy, I don't know why Towser wants me to spend more time with her for she is never there when I go; always rushing off to the gym and the pool and dinners and cocktails or else she is on the phone. I love Towser so much though, she hugs me a lot and she says things that make me laugh and she gives me wonderful presents. Do you know she made Joyce bake a chocolate cake for me? And my new bracelet is so lovely. It's my birthstone you know, Mummy. You know what, Grandma Elaine, I mean Towser says she is going to talk to you about taking me to see my cousins Jason and Maureen in Clearwater when she goes to do her Christmas shopping in Miami. Oh Mummy, can I go? You know all the girls in my class have been to Miami and you've never taken me. Mum, can we go to Disneyworld soon? I'm so ashamed everyone in school has been to Disneyworld and I haven't gone yet. When Towser goes out Joyce and I sit in the den and watch TV the whole time except I usually fall asleep during the late show but Joyce watches everything until TV signs off, and next morning when she is making me breakfast she tells me all the parts that I missed. Mummy, can't we get a video? Everyone in my class has a video at home except me. You know Towser is getting a video she says she is getting Mr Kincaid to give her one as a present. Towser is so much fun. Except Mummy, what does she have against my hair? And my skin? She always seems angry about it and Joyce says Grandma is sorry I came out dark because she is almost a white lady and I am really dark. But Mummy what is wrong with that? When I hold my hand next to Joyce my skin is not as dark as hers or Grandma Del's or Daddy's even. Is dark really bad, Mummy?

III

Mummy, did you know that a whistling woman and a crowing hen are an abomination to the Lord? That's what Grandma Del told me and Pearlie when Pearlie was teaching me to whistle. Don't tell Grandma but I can whistle. Want to hear me? –! –! –! Ha ha. Mummy, can you whistle? Pearlie is my best friend in the country she lives near to Grandma in this tiny house so many of them and all the children sleep together in one room on the floor and Mummy, you know what? Pearlie has only one pair of shoes and one good dress and her school uniform though she hardly goes to school and some old things she wears around the house that have holes in them. Can you imagine? And you should see her little brothers! Half the time they are wearing no clothes at all. Mummy can you send Pearlie some of my dresses and some of my toys but not my Barbie doll? She doesn't have any toys at all, not a single one.

And Pearlie is just a little older than me and she has to look after her little brothers when her Mummy goes out to work. She has to feed them and bathe them and change them and while she is changing the baby's nappies her little brothers get into so much trouble. And when they break things when her mother comes home she beats Pearlie. Poor Pearlie! She can balance a pan of water on her head no hands you know. I wish I could do that. She goes to the standpipe for water and carries the pan on her head without spilling a drop. Sometimes I go with her; I borrow a pan and though it's smaller than Pearlie's I always end up spilling the water all over me and the pan gets heavier and heavier till I can hardly bear it before we get to Pearlie's house. Pearlie can wash clothes too. I mean real clothes, not dolly clothes. Really. Her baby brother's nappies and things and she cooks dinner for them but the way they eat is really funny. They don't have a real kitchen or anything she has three big rocks in the fireplace and she catches up a fire when she is ready and she has to fan it and fan it with an old basket top and there is a lot of smoke. It makes me sneeze. Then when the fire is going she puts on a big pot of water and when it is boiling she peels things and throws them in the water to cook – yams and cocos and green bananas and that's what they eat, no meat or rice or salad or anything. Pearlie uses a sharp knife just like a big person and she peels the bananas ever so fast, she makes three cuts and goes zip! zip! with her fingers and the banana is out of its skin and into the pot. She says you must never put bananas and yams to boil in cold water for they will get drunk and never cook. Did you know that?

Once I helped her to rub up the flour dumplings but my dumplings came out so soft Pearlie said they were like fla-fla and she won't let me help her make dumplings again. Pearlie has to do all these things and we only get to play in the evenings when her mother comes home and can you imagine, Mummy, Pearlie has never seen TV? And she has never been to the movies. Never. Mummy do you think Pearlie could come and live with us? I could take her to the movies though I don't know who would look after her baby brothers when her mother goes to work. You know Pearlie doesn't have a father? She doesn't know where he is. I'd die without my Daddy. Grandma Del says I'm to be careful and not spend too much time with Pearlie for Pearlie is beginning to back-chat and is getting very force-ripe. Mummy, what is force-ripe?

Sometimes I play with Eulalie's baby. His name is Oral and he is fat and happy and I help to change his nappy. He likes me a lot and claps his hands when he sees me and he has two teeth already. He likes to grab hold of my hair and we have a hard time getting him to let go. Mummy why can't I have a baby brother to play with all the time? Eulalie and Ermandine love to comb my hair and play with it they say I am lucky to have tall hair but Grandma Del doesn't like Eulalie and Ermandine any more. She says they are a disgraceful Jezebel-lot and dry-eye and bring down shame on their father and mother who try so hard with them. Sometimes my Grandma talks like that and I really don't understand and when I ask her to explain she says, 'Cockroach nuh bizniz inna fowl roos' and she acts real mad as if I did something wrong and I don't know why she is so vexed sometimes and quarrels with everyone even me. She scares me when she is vexed.

You know when Grandma Del is really happy? When she is baking cakes and making pimento liquor and orange marmalade and guava jelly. On, she sings and she gets Emmanuel to make up a big fire out in the yard and she gets out this big big pot and we peel and we peel guava – hundreds of them. When we make stewed guava she gives me a little spoon so I can help to scoop out the seeds and I have to be real careful to do it properly and not break the shells. Mummy, right here you have this little glass jar full of stewed guavas from Grandma Del that I helped to make. Grandma gets so happy to see her kitchen full of these lovely glass jars full of marmalade and guava jelly. But you know what? Grandma just makes it and then she gives it all away. Isn't that funny? And one time she baked a wedding cake and decorated it too – three cakes in different sizes she made and then she put them one on top of the other. Grandma is so clever. She allowed me to help her stir the cake mix in the bowl but it was so heavy I could barely move the spoon. When it was all finished she let me use my fingers to lick out all the mixing bowls. Yum Yum. Why don't you bake cakes so I can lick out the bowls, Mummy?

And this time I found that I had grown so much I couldn't get into the church dresses Grandma made for me last time and Grandma made me some new dresses and she says she will give the old dresses to Pearlie. Mummy can you believe that everyone in church remembered me? And they said: 'WAT-A-WAY-YU-GROW' and 'HOW-IS-YU-DAADIE?' and 'HOW-IS-YU-MAAMIE?' till I was tired. Mummy that is the way they talk, you know, just like Richie and the gardener next door. 'WAT A-WAY-YU-GROW'. They don't speak properly the way we do, you know. Mummy, Eulalie and Ermandine don't go to church or school any more and Ermandine says when I come back next year she will have a little baby for me to play with too and Eulalie says she will have a new little baby.

IV

Mummy, you know what the girls in school say? They say I am the prettiest girl in school and I can be Miss Jamaica. When I'm big I'll go to the gym like you so I can keep my figure and I must take care of my skin for even though I have excellent skin, Towser says, I must always care for it. Towser spends hours before the mirror every morning caring for her skin and her new boyfriend Mr Samuels is always telling her how beautiful she looks. Towser really loves that. Mr Samuels is taking her to Mexico for the long Easter weekend and Towser is going to Miami to buy a whole new wardrobe for the trip. She says she is going to bring me all the new movies for the video. Mummy, when I am old like Grandma will men tell me I'm beautiful too? Can I have my hair relaxed as soon as I am twelve as you promised? Will you allow me to enter Miss Jamaica when I am old enough? You know Jason likes me a lot but he's my cousin so he doesn't count. Mom, am I going to Clearwater again this Christmas to spend time with Jason and Maureen? Maureen is always fighting with me you know but Jason says she's jealous because she isn't pretty like me, she's fat and has to wear braces on her teeth. Will I ever have to wear braces? Mom, when I go to Miami can I get a training bra. All the girls in my class are wearing them and a make-up starter kit? Mom, when are we going to get a Dish?

V

Mom, do I have to go to Grandma Del's again? It's so boring. There's nothing to do and nobody to talk to and I'm ashamed when my friends ask me where I'm going for the holidays and I have to tell them only to my old grandmother in the country. You know Gina is going to Europe and Melody-Ann is spending all of her holidays in California and Jean-Ann is going to her Aunt in Trinidad? Mom, even though Grandma Del has electricity now she has only a small black and white TV set and I end up missing *everything* for she doesn't want me to watch the late show even on weekends, and Grandma's house is so small and crowded and dark and she goes around turning off the lights and at nights Grandma smells because she is always rubbing herself with liniment for her arthritis she says and it's true Grandma is in terrible pain sometimes. Mummy what is going to happen to Grandma when she is real old? She's all alone there.

She got mad at me when I told her I didn't want her to rub castor oil in my hair any more because I was having it conditioned and the castor oil smells so awful. And on Sundays Grandma still wants me to go to church with her. It's so boring. We have to *walk* to church and back. It's miles in the hot sun. I can't walk on the gravel road in my heels. If a parent passed and saw me there among all the country bumpkins I would die and Grandma says I am far too young to be wearing heels even little ones and I tell Grandma I'm not young any more. I'll be entering high school next term and everybody is wearing heels. She criticises everything I do as if I am still a baby and she doesn't like me wearing lip gloss or blusher though I tell her you allow me to wear them. And Grandma still wants me to come and greet all her friends, it's so boring as soon as somebody comes to the house she calls me and I have to drop whatever I am doing, even watching TV, and I have to say hello to all these stupid people. It's so boring Mom you wouldn't believe it, there's nobody but black people where Grandma lives and they don't know anything, they ask such silly questions. And they are dirty. You know this girl Pearlie I used to play with when I was little she is so awful-looking, going on the road with her clothes all torn up and you should see her little brothers always dirty and in rags with their noses running. I can't stand to have them around me and Pearlie and everybody is always begging me clothes and things and I can't stand it so I don't even bother to go outside the house half the time. When anybody comes I can see them through the louvres and I just pretend I am not there or I am sleeping. And everybody is just having babies without being married like Pearlie's mother and they are not ashamed. The worst ones are those two sisters Eulalie and Ermandine, you can't imagine how many babies they have between them a new one every year and Grandma says not a man to mind them.

But Mummy, something terrible happened. That Eulalie and I got into an argument. She's so ignorant and I told her that it was a disgrace to have babies without being married and she said, 'Who says?' and I said, 'Everybody. My Mummy and Grandma Elaine and Grandma Del for a start.' And she said, 'Grandma Del? Yes? You ever hear that she that is without sin must cast the first stone?' And I said, 'What do you mean?' And she said, 'Ask your Grannie Del Miss High-And-Mighty since her son turn big-shot and all. Ask her who his father? And why she never turn teacher? And why her daddy almost turn her out of the house and never speak to her for five years? And why they take so long to let her into Mothers' Union?' And Eulalie wouldn't tell me any more and they were so awful to me they started singing 'Before A married an' go hug up mango tree, A wi' live so. Me one'. You know that song, Mummy? I went home to ask Grandma Del what Eulalie meant, but Mummy, when I got home it was just weird I got so scared that I got this terrible pain in my tummy, my tummy hurt so much I couldn't ask Grandma Del anything and then when I felt better, I couldn't bring myself to say anything for I'm scared Grandma Del will get mad. But Mummy, do you think Grandma Del had Daddy without getting married? Is that what Eulalie meant? Mummy, wouldn't that make Daddy a bastard?

VI

Mummy, please don't send me back to stay with Auntie Rita in Clearwater again. Ever. Nothing, Mummy... It's that Maureen. She doesn't like me.

Mummy, am I really a nigger? That's what Maureen said when we were playing one day and she got mad at me and she said, 'You're only a goddamn nigger you don't know any better. Auntie Evie married a big black man and you're his child and you're not fit to play with me.' Mummy, I gave her such a box that she fell and I didn't care. I cried and cried and cried and though Auntie Rita spanked Maureen afterwards and sent her to bed without any supper I couldn't eat my supper for I had this pain in my tummy such a terrible pain and Uncle Rob came into the bedroom and held my hand and said that Maureen was a naughty girl and he was ashamed of her and *he* thought I was a very beautiful, lovely girl...

But Mummy, how can I be beautiful? My skin is so dark, darker than yours and Maureen's and Jason's and Auntie Rita's. And my hair is so coarse not like yours or Maureen's but then Maureen's father is white. Is that why Maureen called me a nigger? I hate Maureen. She is fat and ugly and still wearing braces...

Mummy, why can't I have straight hair like Maureen? I'm so ashamed of my hair. I simply can't go back to Clearwater.

VII

Mom, I don't care what Dad says I can't go to stay with Grandma Del this summer because the Charm Course is for three weeks and then remember Towser is taking me to Ochi for three weeks in her new cottage. Do you think Towser is going to marry Mr Blake? Then I am going with you to Atlanta. You promised. So I really don't have any time to spend with Grandma this summer. And next holidays remember, you said I can go to Venezuela on the school trip? I don't know what Dad is going on about because if he feels so strongly why doesn't he go and spend time with his mother? Only that's a laugh because Daddy doesn't have time for anybody any more, I mean, is there a time nowadays when he is ever at home? I know Grandma Del is getting old and she is all alone but she won't miss me, she quarrels with me all the time I am there. Mom, I just can't fit her in and that is that.

OK. You know what? I have an idea. Why don't we just take a quick run down to see Grandma this Sunday and then we wouldn't have to worry about her again till next year. Daddy can take us and we can leave here real early in the morning though I don't know how I am going to get up early after Melody-Ann's birthday party Saturday night, but we don't have to stay long with Grandma Del. We can leave there right after lunch so we will be back in time to watch *Dallas*. Eh, Mom?

Olive Senior

Working on The Two Grandmothers

This story is set in Jamaica and Florida. It is told as a monologue by a little girl to her mother. Each section represents a different age in the girl's life and in each she tells her mother about her stay with one of the grandmothers. The story begins when the girl is about five and ends when she is about sixteen.

─────────────────────────── **Before reading** ───────

1. Grandparents
● In pairs, draw family trees to help you talk about your own grandparents. Use the following to help you get going:

– where did they live and are they still alive?
– do your parents tell stories of what your grandparents were like as parents?
– what are your memories of them when you were a small child?
– if you still see them, what is your relationship like with them now you are older?
– how different are your paternal and maternal grandparents from each other? Do they get on with each other?

─────────────────────────── **During reading** ───────

Reading the story : Section I – Grandma Del
2. Characters and places
● What do you learn about Grandma Del from this section? Make a spidergram to show what you've noticed, along with short quotes from the text. An example has been started for you.

She lives somewhere very rural – 'no T.V. And it's very, very dark. No street lights.'

She is the paternal grandmother 'big oval picture frames of ... Daddy as a baby

3. Language
The style of the writing used here is like the voice of a small child.
● List some of the features of the language that Olive Senior has used to create this effect. You might think about the following:

– tone of voice
– length of sentences
– pace
– special phrases
– misunderstandings
– things of interest to the child

Reading the story: Section II – Grandma Elaine (Towser)
4. Characters and places
● Talk about and make a spidergram to show what you learn about Grandma Elaine and where she lives from this section.

5. Tensions between the two grandmothers
● What is Grandma Elaine's view of Grandma Del? Make a list of some of her comments about Grandma Del and talk about possible reasons for her feeling like this.

Reading the story: Section III – Grandma Del
6. Pearlie
● What is the narrator's attitude to Pearlie?
● What does the inclusion of Pearlie add to our understanding of the differences between the two grandmothers in this story?

Reading the story: Section IV – Grandma Elaine (Towser)
7. Key words
In this short section we get a glimpse of what is important to the narrator at this stage in her life.
● Make a scatter diagram of some key words to show this.
● How old do you think she is at this stage in the story? Are the things that are important to her to do with her age or to do with something else?

Reading the story : Section V – Grandma Del
8. Changing attitudes
● Look at the quotes taken from this section. For each one find an earlier quote in the story that will illustrate how much and in what ways the narrator's attitudes have changed.

> 'I'm ashamed when my friends ask me where I'm going for the holidays and I have to tell them only to my old grandmother in the country ...'

> 'Grandma's house is so small and crowded ...'

> 'she only has a small black and white TV set and I end up missing *everything* ...'

> 'I have to say hello to all these stupid people ...'

> 'We have to *walk* to church and back ...'

> 'there's nobody but black people where Grandma lives ...'

> 'Pearlie and everybody is always begging me clothes and things ...'

> 'And everyone is just having babies without being married ...'

Reading the story : Sections VI and VII
9. The final sections
- In small groups talk about your reactions to the two sections which end this story.
- What do we learn about the complicated race issues going on in this story?
- Agree three points that you think the writer is making by ending her story this way.

After reading

10. Dramatisation
- In pairs prepare a dramatisation of the final section in which both the narrator and her mother take part and speak.

11. Questions
Many of the sections end on a question. Talk about the nature of these questions and the effect each has on the section and the story as a whole.

12. Cultural conflict and change

The two grandmothers represent different or changing cultures. Culture in this sense would include 'inherited ideas, beliefs, values, knowledge, activities and traditions transmitted and reinforced by members of the group' (a dictionary definition).

● Make a chart like the one below to show the ways in which the two grandmothers represent different cultures in the story.

	Grandma Del	Grandma Elaine (Towser)
Places		
Language		
Food		
Values, beliefs		
Social pursuits and pastimes		
Attitudes to childhood		

● What is the intention and effect of structuring the story in the way that the author does?
● Olive Senior says that this story is partly about the Americanisation of values. Do you think she considers this to be a good thing or a bad thing? What evidence can you find in the story to support your views?

13. Comparative work – choosing a culture

● How do other writers deal with young people choosing a culture or having to leave one behind? Two stories to look at are 'Joebell and America' and 'My Son the Fanatic'.

14. Comparative work – young people

Look at the suggestions for comparative work after the story 'Kreativ Riting'.

15. Wider reading

● Olive Senior's collections *Summer Lightning and Other Stories* and *Arrival of the Snake Woman and Other Stories* contain more stories about children's experience of their environment and the people around them. Most of the stories are set in rural Jamaica.
● Paule Marshall's 'To Da-Duh, In Memoriam' is a story based on the author's memory of travelling from her home in New York to visit her grandmother in Barbados.
● Maxine Hong Kingston's *Woman Warrior* is a collection of short stories about a Chinese American woman's experience of growing up in two different cultures.
● *The Joy Luck Club* by Amy Tan is a novel telling the story of four Chinese American mothers and their daughters.

● Timothy Mo's *Sour Sweet* is a novel about life in the Chinese community in England.

● Maya Angelou's *I Know Why the Caged Bird Sings* [GCSE] explores the writer's relationship with her mother and father, her brother and grandmother, and her sense of identity and belonging as she moves from the deep south to the northern states of America.

● *The Bluest Eye* by Toni Morrison and *The Color Purple* by Alice Walker also explore society and sexuality through the eyes of young black girls. Both, at times, draw on unusual narrative techniques as does 'The Two Grandmothers'.

Mrs Turner Cutting the Grass

Oh, Mrs Turner is a sight cutting the grass on a hot afternoon in June! She climbs into an ancient pair of shorts and ties on her halter top and wedges her feet into crepe-soled sandals and covers her red-grey frizz with Gord's old golf cap – Gord is dead now, 10 years ago, a seizure on a Saturday night while winding the mantel clock.

The grass flies up around Mrs Turner's knees. Why doesn't she use a catcher, the Saschers next door wonder. Everyone knows that leaving the clippings like that is bad for the lawn. Each fallen blade of grass throws a minute shadow which impedes growth and repair. The Saschers themselves use their clippings to make compost which they hope one day will be ripe as the good manure that Sally Sascher's father used to spread on his fields down near Emerson Township.

Mrs Turner's carelessness over the clippings plucks away at Sally, but her husband Roy is far more concerned about the Killex that Mrs Turner dumps on her dandelions. It's true that in Winnipeg the dandelion roots go right to the middle of the earth, but Roy is patient and persistent in pulling them out, knowing exactly how to grasp the coarse leaves in his hand and how much pressure to apply. Mostly they come up like corks with their roots intact. And he and Sally are experimenting with new ways to cook dandelion greens, believing as they do that the components of nature are arranged for a specific purpose – if only that purpose can be divined.

In the early summer Mrs Turner is out every morning by 10 with her sprinkling can of chemical killer, and Roy, watching from his front porch, imagines how this poison will enter the ecosystem and move by quick capillary surges into his fenced vegetable plot, newly seeded now with green beans and lettuce. His children, his two little girls aged two and four – that they should be touched by such poison makes him morose and angry. But he and Sally so far have said nothing to Mrs Turner about her abuse of the planet because they're hoping she'll go into an old-folks' home soon or maybe die, and then all will proceed as it should.

High-school girls on their way home in the afternoon see Mrs Turner cutting her grass and are mildly, momentarily repelled by the lapped, striated flesh on her upper thighs. At her age. Doesn't she realise? Every last one of them is intimate with the vocabulary of skincare and knows that what has claimed Mrs Turner's thighs is the enemy called cellulite, but they can't understand why she doesn't take the trouble to hide it. It makes them queasy; it makes them fear for the future.

The things Mrs Turner doesn't know would fill the Saschers' new compost pit, would sink a ship, would set off a tidal wave, would make her want to kill herself. Back and forth, back and forth she goes with the electric lawn mower, the grass flying out sideways like whiskers. Oh, the things she doesn't know! She has never heard, for example, of the folk-rock recording star Neil Young, though the high school just around the corner from her house happens to be the very school Neil Young attended as a lad. His initials can actually be seen carved on one of the desks, and a few of the teachers say they remember him, a quiet fellow of neat appearance and always very polite in class. The desk with the initials NY is kept in a corner of Mr Pring's homeroom, and it's considered lucky – despite the fact that the renowned singer wasn't a great scholar – to touch the incised letters just before an exam. Since it's exam time now, the second week of June, the girls walking past Mrs Turner's front yard (and shuddering over her display of cellulite) are carrying on their fingertips the spiritual scent, the essence, the fragrance, the aura of Neil Young, but Mrs Turner is as ignorant of that fact as the girls are that she, Mrs Turner, possesses a first name which is Geraldine.

Not that she's ever been called Geraldine. Where she grew up in Boissevain, Manitoba, she was known always – the Lord knows why – as Girlie Fergus, the youngest of the three Fergus girls and the one who got herself in hot water. Her sister Em went to normal school and her sister Muriel went to Brandon to work at Eatons, but Girlie got caught one night – she was 19 – in a Boissevain hotel room with a local farmer, married, named Gus MacGregor. It was her father who got wind of where she might be and came banging on the door, shouting and weeping, 'Girlie, Girlie, what have you done to me?'

Girlie had been working in the Boissevain Dairy since she'd left school at 16 and had a bit of money saved up, and so, a week after the humiliation in the local hotel, she wrote a farewell note to the family, crept out of the house at midnight and caught the bus to Winnipeg. From there she got another bus down to Minneapolis, then to Chicago and finally New York City. The journey was endless and wretched, and on the way across Indiana and Ohio and Pennsylvania she saw hundreds of towns whose unpaved streets and narrow, blinded houses made her fear some conspiratorial, punishing power had carried her back to Boissevain. Her father's soppy-stern voice sang and sang in her ears as the wooden bus rattled its way eastward. It was summer, 1930.

New York was immense and wonderful, dirty, perilous and puzzling. She found herself longing for a sight of real earth which she assumed must lie somewhere beneath the tough pavement. On the other hand, the brown flat-roofed factories with their little windows tilted skywards pumped her full of happiness, as did the dusty trees, when she finally discovered them, lining the long avenues. Every last person in the world seemed to be outside walking, filling the streets, and every corner breezed with noise and sunlight. She had to pinch herself to believe this was the same sunlight that filtered its way into the rooms of the house back in Boissevain, fading the curtains but nourishing her mother's ferns. She sent postcards to Em and Muriel which said, 'Don't worry about me. I've got a job in the theatre business.'

It was true. For eight-and-a-half months she was an usherette in the Lamar Movie Palace in Brooklyn. She loved her perky maroon uniform, the way it fitted on her shoulders, the way the strips of crinkly, gold braid outlined her figure. With a little flashlight in hand she was able to send streams of light across the furry darkness of the theatre and on to the plum-coloured aisle carpet. The voices from the screen talked on and on. She felt after a time that their resonant declarations and tender replies belonged to her.

She met a man named Kiki in her first month in New York and moved in with him. His skin was as black as ebony. As *black as ebony* – that was the phrase that hung like a ribbon on the end of his name, and it's also the phrase she uses, infrequently, when she wants to call up his memory, though she's more than a little doubtful about what *ebony* is. It may be a kind of stone, she thinks, something round and polished that comes out of a deep mine.

Kiki was a good-hearted man, though she didn't like the beer he drank, and he stayed with her, willingly for several months after she had to stop working because of the baby. It was the baby itself that frightened him off, the way it cried probably. Leaving 50 dollars on the table, he slipped out one July afternoon when Girlie was shopping, and went back to Troy, New York, where he'd been raised.

Her first thought was to take the baby and get on a bus and go find him, but there wasn't enough money, and the thought of the baby crying all the way on the hot bus made her feel tired. She was worried about the rent and about the little red sores in the baby's ears – it was a boy, rather sweetly formed, with wonderful smooth feet and hands. On a murderously hot night, a night when the humidity was especially bad, she wrapped him in a clean piece of sheeting and carried him all the way to Brooklyn Heights where the houses were large and solid and surrounded by grass. There was a house on a corner she particularly liked because it had a wide front porch (like those in Boissevain) with a curved railing – and parked on the porch, its brake on, was a beautiful wicker baby carriage. It was here she placed her baby, giving one last look to his sleeping face, as round and calm as the moon. She walked home, taking her time, swinging her legs. If she had known the word *foundling* – which she didn't – she would have bounded along on its rhythmic back, so airy and wide did the world seem that night.

Most of these secrets she keeps locked away inside her mottled thighs or in the curled pinkness of her genital flesh. She has no idea what happened to Kiki, whether he ever went off to Alaska as he wanted to or whether he fell down a flight of stone steps in the silverware factory in Troy, New York, and died of head injuries before his 30th birthday. Or what happened to her son – whether he was bitten that night in the baby carriage by a rabid cat or whether he was discovered the next morning and adopted by the large, loving family who lived in the house. As a rule, Girlie tries not to think about the things she can't even guess at. All she thinks is that she did the best she could under the circumstances.

In a year she saved enough money to take the train home to Boissevain. She took with her all her belongings, and also gifts for Em and Muriel, boxes of hose, bottles of apple blossom cologne, phonograph records. For her mother she took an embroidered apron and for her father a pipe made of curious gnarled wood. 'Girlie, my Girlie,' her father said, embracing her at the station. Then he said, 'Don't ever leave us again,' in a way that frightened her and made her resolve to leave as quickly as possible.

But she didn't go far the second time around. She and Gordon Turner – he was, for all his life, a tongue-tied man, though he did manage a proper proposal – settled down in Winnipeg, first in St Boniface where the rents were cheap and then Fort Rouge and finally the little house in River Heights just around the corner from the high school. It was her husband Gord who planted the grass that Mrs Turner now shaves in the summertime. It was Gord who trimmed and shaped the caragana hedge and Gord who painted the little shutters with the cut-out hearts. He was a man who loved every inch of his house, the wide wooden steps, the oak door with its glass inset, the radiators and the baseboards and the snug sash windows. And he loved every inch of his wife, Girlie, too, saying to her once, and only once, that he knew about her past (meaning Gus MacGregor and the incident in the Boissevain Hotel), and that as far as he was concerned the slate had been wiped clean. Once he came home with a little package in his pocket: inside was a diamond ring, delicate and glittering. Once he took Girlie on a picnic all the way up to Steep Rock, and in the woods he took off her dress and underthings and kissed every part of her body.

After he died, Girlie began to travel. She was far from rich, as she liked to say, but with care she could manage one trip every spring.

She has never known such ease. She and Em and Muriel have been to Disneyland as well as Disney World. They've been to Europe, taking a 16-day trip through seven countries. The three of them have visited the South and seen the famous antebellum houses of Georgia, Alabama and Mississippi, after which they spent a week in the city of New Orleans. They went to Mexico one year and took pictures of Mayan ruins and queer, shadowy gods cut squarely from stone. And three years ago they did what they swore they'd never have the nerve to do: they got on an airplane and went to Japan.

The package tour started in Tokyo where Mrs Turner ate, on her first night there, a chrysanthemum fried in hot oil. She saw a village where everyone earned a living by making dolls and another village where everyone made pottery. Members of the tour group, each holding up a green flag so their tour leader could keep track of them, climbed on a little train, zoomed off to Osaka where they visited an electronics factory, and then went to a restaurant to eat uncooked fish. They visited more temples and shrines than Mrs Turner could keep track of. Once they stayed the night in a Japanese hotel where she and Em and Muriel bedded down on floor mats and little pillows stuffed with cracked wheat, and woke up, laughing, with backaches and shooting pains in their legs. That was the same day they visited the Golden Pavilion in Kyoto. The three-storey temple was made of wood and had a roof like a set of wings and was painted a soft old flaky gold. Everybody in the group took pictures – Em took a whole roll – and bought postcards; everybody, that is, except a single tour member, the one they all referred to as the Professor. The Professor travelled without a camera, but jotted notes almost continuously into a little pocket scribbler. He was bald, had a trim body and wore Bermuda shorts, sandals and black nylon socks. Those who asked him learned that he really was a professor, a teacher of English poetry in a small college in Massachusetts. He was also a poet who, at the time of the Japanese trip, had published two small chapbooks based mainly on the breakdown of his marriage. The poems, sadly, had not caused much of a stir.

It grieved him to think of that paltry, guarded nut-like thing that was his artistic reputation. His domestic life had been too cluttered; there had been too many professional demands; the political situation in America had drained him of energy – these were the thoughts that buzzed in his skull as he scribbled and scribbled, like a man with a fever, in the back seat of a tour bus travelling through Japan.

Here in this crowded, confused country he discovered simplicity and order and something spiritual, too, which he recognised as being authentic. He felt as though a flower, something like a lily, only smaller and tougher, had unfurled in his hand and was nudging along his fountain pen. He wrote and wrote, shaken by catharsis, but lulled into a new sense of his powers.

Not surprisingly, a solid little book of poems came out of his experience. It was published soon afterwards by a well-thought-of Boston publisher who, as soon as possible, sent him around the United States to give poetry readings.

Mostly the Professor read his poems in universities and colleges where his book was already listed on the Contemporary Poetry course. He read in faculty clubs, student centres, classrooms, gymnasiums and auditoriums, and usually, part way through a reading, someone or other would call from the back of the room, 'Give us your Golden Pavilion poem.'

He would have preferred to read his Fuji meditation or the tone poem of the Inner Sea, but he was happy to oblige his audiences, though he felt *A Day at the Golden Pavilion* was a somewhat light piece, even what is sometimes known on the circuit as a 'crowd pleaser'. People (admittedly they were mostly undergraduates) laughed out loud when they heard it; he read it well, too, in a moist, avuncular, amateur actor's voice, reminding himself to pause frequently, to look upwards and raise an ironic eyebrow. The poem was not really about the Golden Pavilion at all, but about three Midwestern lady tourists who, while viewing the temple and madly snapping photos, had talked incessantly and in loud, flat-bottomed voices about knitting patterns, indigestion, sore feet, breast lumps, the cost of plastic raincoats and a previous trip they'd made together to Mexico. They had wondered, these three – noisily, repeatedly – who back home in Manitoba should receive a postcard, what they'd give for an honest cup of tea, if there was an easy way to remove stains from an electric coffee maker, and where they would go the following year, Hawaii?

They were the three Furies, the three witches, who for vulgarity and tastelessness formed a shattering counterpoint to the Professor's own state of transcendence. He had been affronted, angered, half-crazed.

One of the sisters, a little pug of a woman, particularly stirred his contempt, she of the pink pantsuit, the red toenails, the grapefruity buttocks, the overly bright souvenirs, the garish Mexican straw bag containing Dentyne chewing gum, aspirin, breath mints, sun goggles, envelopes of saccharine, and photos of her dead husband standing in front of a squat, ugly house in Winnipeg. This defilement she had spread before the ancient and exquisitely proportioned Golden Pavilion of Kyoto, proving – and here the Professor's tone became grave – proving that sublime beauty can be brought to the very doorway of human eyes, ears and lips and remain unperceived. When he comes to the end of *A Day at the Golden Pavilion* there is generally a thoughtful half-second of silence, then laughter and applause. Students turn in their seats and exchange looks with their fellows. They have seen such unspeakable tourists themselves. There was old Auntie Marigold or Auntie Flossie. There was that tacky Mrs Shannon with her rouge and her jewellery. They know – despite their youth, they know – the irreconcilable distance between taste and banality. Or perhaps that's too harsh; perhaps it's only the difference between those who know about the world and those who don't.

It's true Mrs Turner remembers little about her travels. She's never had much of a head for history or dates; she never did learn, for instance, the difference between a Buddhist temple and a Shinto shrine. She gets on a tour bus and goes and goes, and that's all there is to it. She doesn't know if she's going north or south or east or west. What does it matter? She's having a grand time. And she's reassured, always, by the sameness of the world. She's never heard the word *commonality*, but is nevertheless fused with its sense. In Japan she was made as happy to see carrots and lettuce growing in the fields as she was to see sunlight, years earlier, pouring into the streets of New York City. Everywhere she's been she's seen people eating and sleeping and working and making things with their hands and urging things to grow. There have been cats and dogs, fences and bicycles and telephone poles, and objects to buy and take care of; it is amazing, she thinks, that she can understand so much of the world and that it comes to her as easily as bars of music floating out of a radio.

Her sisters have long forgotten about her wild days. Now the three of them love to sit on tour buses and chatter away about old friends and family members, their stern father and their mother who never once took their part against him. Muriel carries on about her children (a son in California and a daughter in Toronto) and she brings along snaps of her grandchildren to pass round. Em has retired from school teaching and is a volunteer in the Boissevain Local History Museum, to which she has donated several family mementos; her father's old carved pipe and her mother's wedding veil and, in a separate case, for all the world to see, a white cotton garment labelled 'Girlie Fergus Underdrawers, handmade, trimmed with lace, circa 1918'. If Mrs Turner knew the word irony she would relish this. Even without knowing the word irony, she relishes it.

The professor from Massachusetts has won an important international award for his books of poems; translation rights have been sold to a number of foreign publishers; and recently his picture appeared in *The New York Times*, along with a lengthy quotation from *A Day at the Golden Pavilion*. How providential, some will think, that Mrs Turner doesn't read *The New York Times* or attend poetry readings, for it might injure her deeply to know how she appears in certain people's eyes, but then there are so many things she doesn't know.

In the summer, as she cuts the grass, to and fro, to and fro, she waves to everyone she sees. She waves to the high-school girls who timidly wave back. She hollers hello to Sally and Roy Sascher and asks them how their garden is coming on. She cannot imagine that anyone would wish her harm. All she's done is live her life. The green grass flies up in the air, a buoyant cloud swirling about her head. Oh, what a sight is Mrs Turner cutting her grass and how, like an ornament, she shines.

Carol Shields

Working on Mrs Turner Cutting the Grass

1. The first paragraph
● Read the opening paragraph of the story which has been re-printed for you below.

'Oh, Mrs Turner is a sight cutting the grass on a hot afternoon in June! She climbs into an ancient pair of shorts and ties on her halter top and wedges her feet into crepe-soled sandals and covers her red-grey frizz with Gord's old golf cap – Gord is dead now, 10 years ago, a seizure on a Saturday night while winding the mantel clock.'

● From this description of her, in pairs agree three or four statements you could make about Mrs Turner.
● What do you learn about Mrs Turner from the narrator's tone of voice?

2. Mrs Turner's life
● As you read the story, make a list of all of the events that have happened to Mrs Turner in her life.
● When you have finished reading, look down the list and see whether there is any pattern to these events. Look back at the opening paragraph and think about what she was once like and what she is like now.

3. Attitudes to Mrs Turner
We are given a number of different views of Mrs Turner in the course of the story. We hear the view of:

– Sally Sascher
– Roy Sascher
– the high-school girls
– her family when she was a young girl
– her sisters now that she is old
– the Professor
– the people who hear the Professor's poem

- For each one, try to define what kind of view they have:

– critical
– sympathetic
– mocking
– irritated
– concerned
– caring
– distant
– close

- Think about the narrator's view of Mrs Turner and her life. To help you, look back at the opening paragraph, the last paragraph and this extract from the end of the story.

> 'She doesn't know if she's going north or south or east or west. What does it matter? She's having a grand time. And she's reassured, always, by the sameness of the world. She's never heard the word *commonality*, but is nevertheless fused with its sense. In Japan she was made as happy to see carrots and lettuce growing in the fields as she was to see sunlight, years earlier, pouring into the streets of New York City. Everywhere she's been she's seen people eating and sleeping and working and making things with their hands and urging things to grow. There have been cats and dogs, fences and bicycles and telephone poles, and objects to buy and take care of; it is amazing, she thinks, that she can understand so much of the world and that it comes to her as easily as bars of music floating out of a radio.'

- One of the things that alerts the reader to the narrator's attitude is the way she presents the *other* characters in the story. Look at places where the other characters appear in the story and decide what the narrator wants us to think about them and their views on Mrs Turner.

4. What Mrs Turner knows

At one point early in the story the narrator exclaims, 'Oh, the things she doesn't know!' Again, at the end of the story the narrator says, 'but then there are so many things she doesn't know.'
- Look through the story to see what kinds of things Mrs Turner does not know.
- By the end of the story, how has her lack of awareness or understanding of certain things affected your attitude to her as a character?

5. What the story is about

- Work in small groups or pairs. From this list of themes, decide which ones are most clearly explored in the story:

– youth and old age
– knowledge and innocence
– communities and individuals
– which values are important in life
– generosity of spirit contrasted with critical ways of seeing other people

• Choose one theme to explore more fully. Make three or four statements about what the story seems to be saying about that theme and how it does so. For each statement find a piece of evidence from the text itself. Prepare to present your statements and evidence to the rest of the class.

6. Mrs Turner's view

The story gives the reader a lot of information and insight into the character of Mrs Turner but it is written by a narrator, in the third person.

• Try writing the thoughts of Mrs Turner, as she cuts the grass and looks back on her life and considers the people around her. Try to use all the clues about her character to help you. You will need to remember the narrator's comment, 'but then there are so many things she doesn't know.'

7. Comparative work – communities and individuals

Look at the suggestions for comparative work after the short story, 'The Schoolteacher's Guest'.

8. Comparative work – third person narratives

Look at the suggestions for comparative work after the short story, 'A Small Good Thing'.

9. Wider reading

• Carol Shields' novel *The Stone Diaries* is the story of a woman's life, from her birth on the kitchen floor of a house in Manitoba, Canada, to her death in a Florida nursing home. Like 'Mrs Turner Cutting the Grass' it takes an ordinary woman's life and makes it extraordinary.

• Margaret Atwood is another Canadian novelist and short story writer, who writes particularly well about the lives of women. *The Edible Woman*, *Surfacing* and *Lady Oracle* are all novels which take an interesting or unusual angle on women characters.

• Alan Bennett's *Talking Heads* are six monologues, originally written and recorded for BBC TV but also available as a written text. They are amusing, realistic portrayals of six people's personalities and lives. All but one are about women and it would be interesting to compare Alan Bennett and Carol Shields' portrayal of middle-aged women.

Dear George

S he was trying to write an essay on the various sorts of humour in *As You Like It* at the same time, which didn't help. To her right was a pad of file paper on which she scrawled scathing comments about Shakespeare as they occurred. In front of her was her mother's block of Basildon Bond. She had used four sheets so far.

Dear George, she wrote for the fifth time, and added a curly little comma like a tadpole. She sat back and admired the comma. That was pure luck when it turned out like that. Sometimes if you concentrated on something too hard you ruined it.

She sauntered over to the mirror and stared at herself for a few minutes. 'You gorgeous creature you,' she murmured, sly but sincere, ogling herself from sideways on. A yawn overtook her and she watched her tongue arch like a leaf. Then she performed a floozie's bump and grind back to the *Complete Works*.

Jaq: What stature is she of?
Orl: Just as high as my heart.

George was tall, that was the best thing about him. She would be higher than his heart, of course, probably about level with his Adam's apple, but that was good enough for her. Already her feet were seven-and-a-halfs, and she was still not yet fifteen.

She turned back to her latest copy of the letter to George. She knew its phrases by heart now, and they were as spontaneous as two hours' effort could make them. 'Daniel Minter asked me to tell you that the Grindley match has been rearranged for the 16th because he thought you were coming back to the Bio Lab, but you didn't. So I thought I'd drop you a line to let you know. He asked me because I had to be there till five o'clock on the last day of term, collecting the results from our petri dishes.'

The handwriting was vital, that was what she was trying to perfect as she toiled over copy after copy. There must be nothing round or childish about it. She was dabbling now with italics like barbed wire. Sophistication was what she aimed for. A looped *f* would still creep in if she didn't watch it, or a silly swan-backed *s*.

There was her fat little sister, rattling the doorknob to be let in.

'I won't talk,' came the promises through the keyhole. 'I'll just sit on your bed and watch you.'

'Go away,' she drawled. 'You are banal.'

Silence. She thought of her sister's big baffled sheep's eyes and this made her giggle crossly and feel cruel.

'Banal!' she bellowed. 'Look it up in the dictionary.'

Her sister rushed heftily off downstairs towards the bookcase. From another part of the house drifted a weak howl from their mother, who was trying to get the new baby to sleep.

Disgust jerked her out of her seat. How *could* she, at *her* age, it was so *selfish* of her. It was just showing off. As everyone at school had pointed out, she'd probably been trying for a boy this time, so *served her right*.

She would never be able to bring George home. It would be too awful. Her mother would probably try to breastfeed it in front of him. She started to wriggle and giggle in horror.

Cel: I pray you, bear with me, I cannot go no further.

Tou: For my part, I had rather bear with you than bear you: yet I should bear no cross if I did bear you, for I think you have no money in your purse.

She picked up her pen and scribbled, 'This is obviously meant to be funny, but it is not. It is rubbish. People only say this is good because it is Shakespeare. It is really boring. It is not even grammar, e.g. I cannot go no further.' The hexagonal plastic shaft of the biro turned noisily in the grip of her front teeth as she paused to read through what she had written. Then she crossed out 'boring' and printed 'banal' in its place.

'Commonplace. Trite. Hackneyed,' came through the keyhole with a lot of heavy breathing; then a pause and, 'What do *they* mean?'

'Go away,' she said. 'Ask Mum.'

Served her mother right if she used up all the stamps and Basildon Bond. Spitefully she folded and inserted each of the four early drafts into separate envelopes, sealed them and wrote out George's address four times with self-consciously soppy relish. She had no intention of sending any of them, and stuck on the stamps in a spirit of wicked waste. Later today she would tear them up to show she had style, and send off this perfect fifth version.

She read it through again. It was making her cringe now, she couldn't see it fresh any more. She'd read those phrases so often, she couldn't tell whether they came across as casual or childish or too keen or what.

'I wish I was in 6B with you, all the O-levels out of the way. Hope you have a good holiday. If you would possibly feel like meeting for any reason, I am fairly free this holiday. Maybe hear from you soon. Ciao.'

Was ciao too trendy? She hadn't thought it was till this moment. She couldn't put Yours sincerely, and shook at the thought of Love. Cheers was what the boys in 6B said to each other, but she wouldn't stoop that low.

'Dear George,' she scribbled again, this time on a naughty impulse and a sheet of scrap paper, 'I don't know I could stand to go out with you if Every Time We Said Goodbye you said Chiz instead. Why do you do it? It makes you sound really thick. Chiz chiz chiz chiz chiz. Try Ciao, it's more stylish – it's Italian in case you didn't know and it means the same as chiz – you look a bit Italian which is partly why I fancy you.'

The mournfulness of his image caught her, stopped her ticking for a second or two as a cameo of large meaty nobility filled her mind's eye.

She reread what she had written, then, sniggering, clattering her teeth together in enamelled applause, dipping her head down so that her hair piled up on one side of the paper in a foresty rustle, she scrawled, 'You can't be *that* thick. Anyone can have bad luck in O-levels, ha ha, though two retakes in history is a bit much.'

Cupping her chin on the half shell of her hands, she made her mouth into a kissing shape. With the tip of her tongue she tenderly tapped inside each of the teeth in her upper jaw.

'I would like to feel your hands on the back of my waist (25"), with the thumbs round my sides,' she scrawled, chewing invisible gum, 'but only if they aren't sweaty. If you have wet hands it's all over before it's started, sorry Gorgeous George but that's the way I am.'

Holding her hands up in front of her, using them like boned fans to block the light, she spotted an incipient hangnail poking up from the cuticle of her left thumb and fell on it like a falcon, tearing at it with famished energy. When she had made it bleed she lost interest and stared out of the window.

There on the back lawn her galumphing little sister was helping their mother hang out baby vests and babygros and other baby rubbish in the sun. Her mother had it strapped to her front in a hideous pink nylon sling.

'No style,' she muttered, curling her lip. She pulled the curtains on them and made a warm gloom.

Once the candle was lit and positioned on her homework table, she was able to ignore the worst aspects of her room, like the brainlessly 'cheerful' duvet cover with its sun, moon and poppy field. Her face's reflection was a blanched heart in the mirror on the back wall. When she came home on the last train she saw her reflection in the window like that, pale and pointed, looking sideways, fleering at the bugle eyes which were so very blot-like and black above cream-coloured cheeks. She had a vision of George coming up to her as she sat illegally alone in her accustomed first-class carriage, and saw his difficult smile.

Hugging herself as she rocked to and fro on the folding chair, adjusting her balance as it threatened to jack-knife her thighs to stomach in its fold-up maw, her hands became George's, firm and pressing around her waist. She stood up.

Now one crept forward and undid the buttons of her shirt, stroked her neck down past the collar bone. Catching sight of herself in the mirror tweaking her own breast, the silly lost expression left her face instantly.

She reached across for Shakespeare and flicked through until she came to her latest discovery in *Antony and Cleopatra.* Holding her left hand palm out to her reflection, she touched wrist to wrist in the chill glass and murmured,

> There is gold and here
> My bluest veins to kiss, a hand that kings
> Have lipped, and trembled kissing.

This produced a reluctant simper and a slow shudder which wriggled through from head to foot finishing with a sigh. After a minute she tried it again but this time it did not work.

Lifting her knees and pointing her toes like a cartoon of stealth, she fell back onto her *As You Like It* essay with an angry groan.

> It was a lover and his lass,
> With a hey, and a ho, and a hey nonino
> That o'er the green corn field did pass
> In the spring time, the only pretty ring time
> When birds do sing, hey ding a ding ding.

'Anybody could write this sort of stuff,' she wrote. 'If Madonna put it in one of her lyrics, English teachers everywhere would say, how moronic.' Then she dashed off an inspired demolition job on Touchstone before losing her drift.

Flicking through the rice-paper leaves, she came to another juicy bit.

> Des: 0, banish me, my lord, but kill me not!
> Oth: Down, strumpet!
> Des: Kill me tomorrow; let me live tonight!
> Oth: Nay, if you strive –

There was George, big George, looming like a tower in the half-dark, and herself in a white nightdress with pintucks from shoulder seam to waist, quite plain, no lace, his hot hands round her neck... She inhaled slowly and closed her eyes; leaned forward and pressed a bit against her windpipe with her thumbs; blushingly smirked; then felt a chill tinge of shame, a prickling under her arms like cactus hairs, and busily started to biro a blue swallow on the inside of her elbow.

Tattoos only lasted when the ink got into your bloodstream.

Maybe she would get her ears pierced this afternoon at Shangri La, she thought, though that was supposed to hurt a lot too, there was no anaesthetic, they just shot a spike through the lobe with a little gun like a paper punch.

She sniggered as she remembered something rude. According to Valerie Mitchell from 6B, who was a Saturday girl at Shangri La and who was doing

Louis XIV for a special project, the Sun King's bed was heaped with pillows stuffed with his mistresses' hair. 'And not with the hair from their *heads*,' Valerie had leered.

Now she described this conversation to George in her make-believe letter, and even enclosed a clipping to launch his collection. When it came to signing off this time, she added fifty smacking Xs. She then spat on the paper before smearing it with her fist. Across the envelope's seal she wrote SWALK in lipstick and from the Queen's mouth on the stamp she drew a balloon saying, 'Who's a pretty boy then.'

'*Please* come and play,' whined her sister from the other side of the door. 'You've been up here for ages now and I don't believe you're just doing revision.'

'Go away,' she said.

'We could go roller skating,' said her sister.

'Mum won't let me go out till I've done the washing up,' she said, 'and I'm refusing on moral grounds since it's not my turn, so *I can't* go out.'

Once her sister had gone stump-stump-stumping off downstairs, she crept along the landing, pausing to stare and bite her thumb at the rumpled bedroom shared by her mother and stepfather. Then, when she was safely locked in the bathroom, she transferred all the plastic ducklings, sailors, mechanically spouting whales and dinghies from the bath to the lavatory and closed the lid on them.

During the chin-high soak which followed, she lay poaching in water so hot that a clear Plimsoll line appeared on her skin, all fiery lobster-coloured flesh below the water's surface while above stayed white and sweat-pearled. The little bathroom was dense with steam, the wallpaper's paisley invisible and the gloss-painted ceiling lustrous with moisture. She closed her eyes and saw George opening her letter, his crooked smile, his reaching for the telephone. They talked with sophisticated ease, and soon they were sharing a fondue down at the Mousetrap.

There was silence except for the rustle from the boa of weightless scented bubbles sitting on her shoulders. It came into her mind that it would be much more natural to give him a ring straight off, and she decided not to send the letter after all.

When at last she tottered back, lurid and wrinkled and dizzy, her sister was sitting on the bed.

'You've got to play with me now,' said her sister. 'I've done all your washing up and Mum says you're horrible but you can go out on condition you take me roller skating.'

'Shift up,' she croaked, collapsing onto the bed, clutching at disappearing shreds of George as the towels came adrift all round her.

'So you *will* come when you're dry,' said her sister, gnat-like. 'I've got your skates out. I've tidied your room, see, so Mum won't go on about that either. There's no excuse. I even went down the road to post your letters.'

'Letters,' she said stupidly, still stunned by the equatorial bath, before it dawned on her.

Helen Simpson

Working on Dear George

1. Reactions to the story
● Discuss whether you agree or disagree with the following statements about the story:

– teenage girls are just like this
– family life is just like this
– this is a funny portrayal of a teenage girl
– this is a patronising portrayal of a teenage girl

2. The characterisation of the girl
Nothing much happens in this story, but the writer manages to give us an intimate picture of a fourteen year old girl. She does this by focusing closely on what the girl does, thinks, writes and says in about two hours of her life.
● Select a few short quotes which show the writer's methods, and note down alongside what this adds to your knowledge of the character of the girl. A couple have been done for you to get you started.

What she does/ says/thinks/writes	What this tells us about the girl
'pausing to stare and bite her thumb at the rumpled bedroom shared by her mother and stepfather'	Her mother's relationship with her stepfather is something she is very aware of and maybe dislikes
'Her mother would probably try to breastfeed it in front of him.'	

3. Style – your own writing
The next day, George receives five copies of the same letter and one copy of a letter written on a scrap of paper with fifty kisses on the bottom.
● Use this scenario as an idea for your own writing, in which you show the kind of boy George is and his reactions to these letters. Keep to some of the constraints Helen Simpson uses in her own story:

– keep the character in one place
– make the story take place within a short time-frame
– focus only on thoughts, actions and a few spoken words for characterisation

4. A radio play
● Try turning this story into a 10-minute radio play, in which the central character's thoughts and emotions are spoken aloud. Alan Bennett has written a series of TV monologues called *Talking Heads* that you might like to look at first. Think about these issues:

– how could sound effects be used to dramatise the girl's actions, feelings and emotions?
– could you use other voices, such as friends, her sister etc., to bring her thoughts to life?
– which elements of the story might you have to leave out? Are there other details you could invent to create a similar effect, without changing the meaning of the story?

5. Comparative work – young people
Look at the suggestions for comparative work after the story 'Kreativ Riting'.

6. Wider reading
● 'You Should Have Seen the Mess' by Muriel Spark is a short story written in the voice of a young woman entering adult life. The story creates a strong sense of her personality and values.
● *Gregory's Girl,* a play by Bill Forsyth, shows an adolescent boy's first love affair. There is a lively film version of the play.
● *P'Tang Yang Kipperbang* is a play by Jack Rosenthal about the experience of growing up.
● *Catcher in the Rye*, a 1950s American novel by J.D. Salinger, is seen through the eyes of a teenage boy who is disaffected with school, parents and life.
● *The Secret Diary of Adrian Mole aged 13¾*, by Sue Townsend is a witty look inside the mind of a teenage boy.

The Writers and Their Stories

Brian Aldiss was born in East Dereham, in England in 1925. He served in India and the Far East during the Second World War, then worked as a bookseller, as Literary Editor of The Oxford Mail and as a writer and critic. He has written many novels and collections of short stories in the science fiction genre and has won several literary awards. He has been President of the British Science Fiction Association. His best known novels are the trilogy *Helliconia Spring* (1982), *Helliconia Summer* (1983) and *Helliconia Winter* (1985). He has also written non-fantastic fiction, non-fiction and poetry.

Brian Aldiss on 'Headless'

This short story came full-born into my mind one morning. I was shaving – with an electric, not a cut-throat, razor. After breakfast, I went to my computer and entered the story, filling in details as I went along.

Does this sound easy? Yes, in a way it was easy, but it came from a well-furnished mind. Notice how international the story is. I had just returned from a visit to Turkmenistan, in Central Asia. I have also visited the other countries mentioned, Germany, Sweden, etc., and have noted how competitive they all are (Britain included) on the European stage. And of course I observe the arrogance of pop stars, yelling and prancing in front of their microphones. My chief character will also do anything to be famous.

'Headless' gains its dynamism from our humanity. Despite the title of the tale, we hope the poor fellow will not lose his head. We hope the writer will not be that beastly.

So the story is about human weakness. But it does not moralise. It is, in fact, a funny story. It is up to the reader to perceive its moral.

Isabel Allende is a Chilean novelist. As the daughter, and later the step-daughter of a diplomat, she travelled widely during her childhood. She worked as a journalist in Chile for many years, and became a newscaster and host of TV chat shows. Her uncle was the first democratically elected Marxist president in Latin America. A military coup in Chile resulted in his overthrow and death. Isobel Allende was forced to flee the military regime that took control. She emigrated to Venezuela with her husband and children. Her first work of fiction, *The House of Spirits*, was published in 1981 and was a worldwide bestseller. She has since written other novels, *Of Love and Shadows* (1985), *Eva Luna* (1987), and a collection of stories, *The Stories of Eva Luna*. Her most recent work, *Paula* is an autobiographical work about the death of her daughter.

Peter Carey was born in Australia in 1943 and now lives in New York. He has written four novels, including *Illywhacker*, which was shortlisted for the Booker Prize in 1985, and *Oscar and Lucinda* which won the Booker Prize in 1988. 'American Dreams' is taken from his collection of stories, *The Fat Man in History*.

Peter Carey on 'American Dreams'

This is one of a number of short stories ('The Fat Man in History' is another) which were inspired by my experiences back-packing through Sumatra, Java and Bali in the early 1970s. So there is a way in which this is an Indonesian story – it began with me wondering what it would feel like to be an Indonesian living in a village, having foreigners come to stare and take my photograph. I went home and wrote this story which is set, not in an Indonesian village, but in a small Australian town very like the one I grew up in.

At that time there was no international tourism in Australia, and so the idea that tourists would come and look at us was quite bizarre. Now, tourists fly to Australia from all over the world, so that particular aspect of the story has been lost.

Raymond Carver was born in Oregon, USA, in 1938. His father was a saw-mill worker and his mother was a waitress and clerk. He married young and much of his early adult life was spent working to earn a living for his family. He did all kinds of jobs, including being a hospital porter, a delivery man and a petrol station attendant. During this time he became an alcoholic and eventually his marriage broke up. Although he started writing in the early 1960s and '70s, it was only in 1976 that he began to receive attention and acclaim as a writer. He gave up drinking and began living with the poet, Tess Gallagher, with whom he remained until his death in 1988. Much of his writing focuses on the experiences of his early adult life, when he was struggling to earn a living and there were desperate problems in his marriage. He is best known for his short stories, which have been collected in *Where I'm Calling from*. The film *Short Cuts* by Robert Altman, is an adaptation of stories by Carver, including 'A Small Good Thing'. These stories have now been published by Harvill Press, under the title *Short Cuts*.

Mary Flanagan was born and brought up in New Hampshire. After doing a degree in History of Art, she worked in publishing in New York for three years. Her collection of short stories, *Bad Girls*, was published in 1984 and she has written two novels, *Trust* (1987) and *Rose Reason* (1991). She now lives in London.

Mary Flanagan on 'White Places'

When I was a child in New Hampshire (USA), my best friends were my cousins Karen and Jean. We were born only fifteen months apart and felt more like triplets than cousins. But, as sometimes happens, the two stronger dominated the younger and more sensitive third, and I'm sorry to say we teased Jeanie mercilessly. Our Gothic imaginations devised elaborate games in which she was forced to play the villain or the victim or both.

Though many years have passed, we are still bound by the dark and magic rituals of childhood as well as the sunlight affection we've always shared. Once Karen visited me in London and I showed her 'White Places' which I'd just finished.

163

After she'd read it she smiled at me and said, 'I see. This is your apology to Jean.'

Two more things. The ending isn't true. And the snow in New Hampshire really can rise to the middle of the ground-floor windows. When it does the schools are closed, and all the children build snow forts.

Janet Frame is a New Zealand novelist, born in 1924 and best known for her autobiographies *To the Is-Land, An Angel at My Table* and *The Envoy from Mirror City*. She spent much of her early adult life in psychiatric hospitals, following the accidental drowning of two of her sisters and several nervous breakdowns. She wrote *The Lagoon and other stories* at the age of 21. It was her first published work. It won a major literary award and this helped her to fight her way out of madness and the stigma of psychiatric treatment. She spent many years abroad, living in Ibiza, Andorra and then England. She has written numerous novels and short stories, many of which deal with ideas about madness. She has won several literary awards and is regarded as New Zealand's most important living writer.

Brian Friel was born in Omagh, in Ireland in 1929. He is best known for his plays, which include *Philadelphia, Here I Come!, Translations* and *Dancing at Lughnasa*. He has also published three anthologies of short stories, *The Saucer of Larks* (1962), *The Gold in the Sea* (1966), and *The Diviner* (1983). Selected stories from these collections have been published in *Selected Stories* by The Gallery Press.

Hanif Kureishi was born and brought up in Bromley, South London in 1954. His mother is English, his father Pakistani and the rest of his family live in Karachi. In 1982 he was appointed Writer in Residence at the Royal Court Theatre. In 1984 he wrote a film screenplay for Channel 4, *My Beautiful Laundrette*. It won an Oscar nomination for Best Screenplay. His second film, *Sammy and Rosie Get Laid*, was also highly successful. His novel *The Buddha of Suburbia* won the Whitbread Prize for Best First Novel in 1990 and was made into a TV drama series for the BBC. His most recent novel *The Black Album*. is a thriller set in the year of the fatwah against Salman Rushdie. The central character is a young student whose family came to England from Pakistan. Like Ali, in *My Son the Fanatic*, he is caught between religious fundementalism and the lifestyle and youth culture of Britain today. *My Son the Fanatic* is currently being adapted as a BBC film.

Ursula Le Guin is an American writer of science fiction, born in Berkeley, California. Her most highly acclaimed work is *The Earthsea Trilogy*, composed of *A Wizard of Earthsea* (1968), *The Tombs of Atuan* (1971), and *The Farthest Shore* (1972). In some of her more recent work she has been highly critical of American political and social values. Her novels reject the traditional science fiction fascination with machinery and technological change and focus instead on people and societies.

Earl Lovelace was born in Trinidad in 1935 and spent his childhood in Tobago and Port of Spain. He worked for a publishing company, then joined the Civil Service and worked for the Forestry Department and the Department of Agriculture. He is best known for his novels, *While the Gods are Falling*, *The Dragon Can't Dance* and *The Wine of Astonishment*. He has also written plays and a collection of stories, *A Brief Conversion and other stories*. His most recent novel is *Salt*, published in September 1996. He lives in Trinidad and teaches creative writing at the University of the West Indies.

Brian McCabe was born in a small mining community near Edinburgh. He has won two Scottish Arts Council Book Awards. He has published two volumes of poetry, a novel, *The Other McCoy* (1990), and two collections of short stories, *The Lipstick Circus* (1985) and *In a Dark Room with a Stranger* (1993). He lives with his family in Edinburgh.

Brian McCabe on 'Kreativ Writing'

In the story I tried to present a kind of worst scenario of a teacher trying to teach creative writing. The teacher himself thinks that writing is something shrouded in mystery, and though he tries to access it imaginatively – using music, lifting some of the normal restrictions – his experiment goes disastrously wrong. It is something of a cautionary tale for teachers, in which I was attempting to explode one or two of the most popular misconceptions about writing and the teaching of writing. I was also trying to get at something more fundamental in the story – how the classroom can become a place of futility for both teacher and pupil when the gulf between the two grows so wide that it is impossible to bridge. Though there is communication going on between P.K. and his charges, it is all negative and combative: he talks down to them, makes fun of them, runs them down; they take the piss out of him, disrupt the lesson as best they can, and ask questions which are deliberately meant to distract everyone's attention from the subject in hand. On the other hand, Pitcairn is trying to do something new and exciting, and Joe Murdoch and his friends have a great deal of openness, vitality and humour. The real problem is that both teacher and pupil are locked into a situation in which they are dedicated to scoring points off each other – this is what has come to matter to them more than anything.

It was a deliberate irony on my part that Joe Murdoch should respond not to the Bach or the 'automatic writing', but to the more pedestrian subject offered, 'Myself as Others See Me.' It was also a deliberate irony on my part that, though his piece of writing isn't at all bad – it is honest, specific, expressive and very revealing – it will be something to be destroyed, at best treated as a joke, and the terrible point of the story, as far as I am concerned, is that he himself sees what he has done in this way.

Colum McCann was born in Dublin in 1965. He is the author of a collection of short stories, *Fishing the Sloe-Black River*, and a novel, *SongDogs*. He has won the Hennessy Award for Irish Writing and the Rooney Prize for Irish Literature. He currently lives in New York with his wife, Allison.

Colum McCann on 'A Basket Full of Wallpaper'
'A Basket Full of Wallpaper' is a story written while living in Japan. My wife and I were staying in a youth hostel in Kyoto. The owner, Mr Tani – a lovely eccentric who could hum every national anthem in the world – became a friend of mine. He let me stay in my tiny room and write while he kicked everyone else out of the hostel. He was interested in my travels to a strange land.

Early in the mornings, when I was woken by chants from a nearby Buddhist monastery, I began to wonder what might have happened if the roles had been reversed. So I invented a story about a Japanese man living in the West of Ireland and the rumours that might leap up around him. The landscape of the imagination is a curious place. For me, it holds more freedom than any reality. I could never have written the true story of myself and Mr Tani. In fact, the main character of the story is not even remotely like Mr Tani. But the story became very important to me, in that I hope it tries to challenge a number of different things: stereotypes, exile, rumour, pity, regret, love and perhaps (to a small degree) that most horrific of our century's moments, Hiroshima.

Olive Senior was born in Jamaica in 1941 and grew up in a rural area of the country. Many of her stories reflect that experience. She has worked in publishing and public relations and has been the editor of the *Jamaica Journal* for a number of years.

In 1987 she was awarded the first Commonwealth Writers Award for *Summer Lightning and other stories* (1986). She has published a collection of poems, *Talking of Trees* (1985), and another book of stories, *Arrival of the Snake Woman and other stories* (1989).

Carol Shields was born in Chicago but has lived in Canada for many years. She is a highly successful novelist. *Mary Swann* was published in Britain in 1990, followed soon after by *Happenstance, The Republic of Love* and *The Stone Diaries*, which was shortlisted for the 1993 Booker Prize.

Carol Shields on 'Mrs Turner Cutting the Grass'
It's always hard to pinpoint exactly where a story began, but in this case I think I know; the connection is quite direct. I heard an acquaintance grumble about a coach trip he took to Greece, and how annoyed he was to find three middle-aged American women standing before the Delphic Oracle and jabbering about trivial domestic concerns. He seemed not to have asked himself who these women really were and why their travel experience was not the same as his.

I've always believed fiction to be about redemption, about trying to see why people are the way they are. When we talk about women of a certain age we often dismiss them as 'the blue rinse girls', or 'the white glove ladies', failing to imagine their inner lives, their former lives, the millions of differences that make each of them unique. I wanted Mrs Turner, with all of her particles of difference, to *shine*.

Helen Simpson has written short stories, a novella and plays for stage and radio. Her first collection of stories, *Four Bare Legs in a Bed*, won the Somerset Maugham short story award and she has been listed as one of *Granta's* Best of Young British Novelists. She lives in London. *Dear George and Other Stories* is her second collection of short stories.

Helen Simpson on 'Dear George'
I'm afraid I can't remember what sparked off 'Dear George'. I think I was trying to remember the manic tedium of writing a homework essay, the idling of the mind and the occasional pounces it makes. I included a few half-hidden Shakespeare jokes for fun (spot the tags from *Hamlet, Romeo and Juliet, King Lear*). I tried to catch the luxury of adolescent boredom, the sense of infinite choice as well as the claustrophobia of being a certain age.